VISCOELASTICITY

A BLAISDELL BOOK IN SOLID MECHANICS

CONSULTING EDITORS

William Prager, *University of California at San Diego*
Joseph Kestin, *Brown University*

VISCOELASTICITY

WILHELM FLÜGGE

STANFORD UNIVERSITY

BLAISDELL PUBLISHING COMPANY

A DIVISION OF GINN AND COMPANY

Waltham, Massachusetts · Toronto · London

Preface

No MATHEMATICAL THEORY can completely describe the complex world around us. Every theory is aimed at a certain class of phenomena, formulates their essential features, and disregards what is of minor importance. The theory meets its limits of applicability where a disregarded influence becomes important. Thus, rigid-body dynamics describes in many cases the motion of actual bodies with high accuracy, but it fails to produce more than a few general statements in the case of impact, because elastic or anelastic deformation, no matter how local or how small, attains a dominating influence.

For a long time mechanics of deformable bodies has been based upon Hooke's law—that is, upon the assumption of linear elasticity. It was well known that most engineering materials like metals, concrete, wood, soil, are not linearly elastic or, are so within limits too narrow to cover the range of practical interest. Nevertheless, almost all routine stress analysis is still based on Hooke's law because of its simplicity.

In the course of time engineers have become increasingly conscious of the importance of the anelastic behavior of many materials, and mathematical formulations have been attempted and applied to practical problems. Outstanding among them are the theories of ideally plastic and of viscoelastic materials. While plastic behavior is essentially nonlinear (piecewise linear at best), viscoelasticity, like elasticity, permits a linear theory. This theory of linear viscoelasticity is the subject of the present book.

The book is intended for an introductory course and for self-study. The reader should be familiar with the basic concepts of mechanics, including stress and strain in two dimensions, and the technique of deriving differential equations from the consideration of the mechanics of an infinitesimal element.

On the mathematical side, the prerequisite is calculus and a brief exposure to complex numbers and to linear ordinary differential equations. In many places the text uses more advanced mathematical methods (Laplace transformation, integral equations, partial differential equations, complex contour integration), but they are explained as far as needed and the reader may postpone their study in depth until later. In Chapter 8 a previous exposure to the theory of elasticity will be helpful.

The book presents the theory of viscoelasticity as an instrument of logical analysis. Basic assumptions are plausibly explained, and mathematical reasoning is used to derive results from them, which are deemed of interest for engineering tasks. There is, however, no reference to specific applications or materials, which, in our fast-changing world, are here today and gone tomorrow, to make room for others.

The exercises, that have been inserted in many places, serve various purposes. Some suggest numerical work leading to results illustrating the physical content of the formulas. Others let the reader come to grips with mathematical techniques of problem solving, introduce additional subject matter, or establish cross connections with related fields in which the reader may have experience. It is suggested that he solve as many of these problems as he can handle, but leave aside those related to an outside field with which he is not sufficiently familiar.

The author wishes to express his thanks to Dr. William Prager for his reading of the manuscript and for his constructive criticism.

Los Altos, California W. Flügge

Contents

VISCOELASTICITY

CHAPTER 1

Introduction

THE MECHANICS OF CONTINUOUS MEDIA deals with three kinds of quantities: stresses, strains, and displacements. *Stresses* describe forces acting inside a body. Usually they are defined as forces (or force components) per unit of area of an infinitesimal section. However, the bending and twisting moments in a plate, the membrane forces in a shell, the bending moment and the shear force in a beam, and the torque in a shaft are also quantities of the same kind. They all describe forces or moments transmitted from one side of a section to the other; and they all come in pairs, equal in magnitude but opposite in sense, as they are acting on both parts of the body separated by the section.

Strains describe local deformations—for example, the increase in length of a line element divided by its original length (tensile strain), or the decrease of the right angle between two line elements (shear strain). There are more sophisticated definitions of strain quantities, like the tensorial strain derived from the change of the square of the line element, or the logarithmic strain. On the other hand, the curvature of a bent beam or plate and the twist of a shaft are also strain quantities, since they describe local change of form without reference to an external coordinate system.

Displacements describe the movement of a point or a line element during the process of deformation, with reference to a fixed coordinate system outside the deformable body. The displacements u, v, and w of the theory of elasticity and the deflection of a beam or a plate are linear displacements; the rotation of a beam element (the "slope" of the textbooks) is an angular displacement.

The stresses, strains, and displacements are connected by three kinds of equations expressing laws of nature:

1

The *equilibrium conditions* are relations between the stress quantities, usually containing their space derivatives. They are written for an infinitesimal element of the body or, occasionally, for a finite part. On the right-hand side they may contain a load quantity. In linear problems these equations do not contain strains or displacements; in nonlinear problems they often do. In problems of dynamics, the equilibrium equations are replaced by the *equations of motion*, which contain second-order time derivatives of the displacements.

Since the deformation of a body is completely known when the displacement of every point is known, it must be possible to calculate the strains from the displacements. Those equations which express the strains in terms of the displacements are known as the *kinematic relations* and are the second set of equations. There is one for each strain quantity.

Depending on the problem, there may be more kinematic relations than displacement components. In this case, it is possible to eliminate the displacements between these equations and thus to arrive at a smaller number of equations, which contain only strains. These are called compatibility equations. They are derived from a more fundamental set, and therefore they are not part of the basic equations.

Neither the conditions of equilibrium nor the kinematic relations depend on the particular material of which the body is made. The influence of this material is expressed by a third set of equations, the *constitutive equations*. They describe the relation between stress and strain. In the simplest case they are six algebraic equations giving the strain components in terms of the stresses, or vice versa. If they are linear, they are known as Hooke's law.

Actual materials show a great variety of behavior. Several idealized materials have been invented which typify various aspects of material behavior. For an elastic material there exists a one-to-one coordination between stress and strain. Many materials show the phenomenon of plastic flow, which may be defined by the following statements: (i). The material is elastic until it reaches the yield limit, that is, until a certain function of the stress components reaches a certain value. (ii). Then additional strain is possible without increase of stress. (iii). This additional strain is permanent, that is, it remains when the stresses are removed. (iv). The time derivative of the strain (the rate of strain) does not appear in the equations.

Some materials show a pronounced influence of the rate of loading, the strain being larger if the stress has grown more slowly to its final value. The same materials display creep, that is, an increasing deformation under sustained load, the rate of strain depending on the stress. Such materials are called *viscoelastic*. Among them are metals at elevated temperatures, concrete, and plastics. & wood.

The constitutive equations of these materials may be either linear or nonlinear. This book develops the linear theory of viscoelasticity.

CHAPTER 2

Viscoelastic Models

THE BEHAVIOR OF viscoelastic materials in uni-axial stress closely resembles that of models built from discrete elastic and viscous elements. We shall see how such models can be used to describe viscoelastic materials and to establish their differential equations.

2.1. The Basic Elements: Spring and Dashpot

Consider a helical spring (Figure 2.1a). When a force P is applied, the length of the spring increases by a certain amount u, and when the force is removed the spring returns to its original length. The same phenomenon is observed in a tension test performed on an elastic bar (Figure 2.1b). We prefer in this case to speak of the stress σ and the strain ϵ, because this removes the particular values of the length and the cross section of the bar from our considerations and thus gives them more generality.

If the material is linear-elastic, we have the relation

$$\sigma = E\epsilon, \tag{2.1}$$

that is, Hooke's law, in which E is Young's modulus.

Now consider the "dashpot" of Figure 2.1c. A piston is moving in a cylinder with a perforated bottom so that no air is trapped inside. Between the cylinder and the piston wall there is a rather viscous lubricant so that a force P is needed to displace the piston. The stronger this force, the faster the piston will move. If the relation is linear, we have $P = k(du/dt)$. A similar deformation may be found in a tension bar of certain materials: When a load is applied, the bar is stretched. However, it is not its elongation ϵl that

3

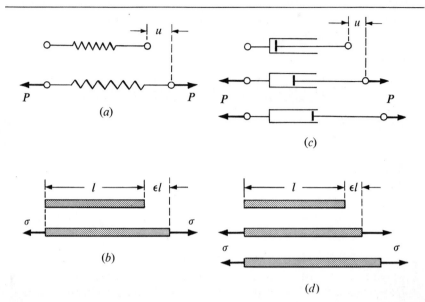

FIGURE 2.1. *Model representation of tension bars—a, b: elastic; c, d: viscous.*

is proportional to the force, but its time rate of change $d(\epsilon l)/dt$. Writing in terms of stress and strain, we have

$$\sigma = F\, d\epsilon/dt = F\, \dot\epsilon. \tag{2.2}$$

Here and elsewhere we shall employ the dot to designate ordinary or partial derivatives with respect to time t. The quantity $\dot\epsilon$ is called the *strain rate*. A material whose stress is proportional to the strain rate is called a *viscous material*.

When (2.2) is translated into shear stress and shear strain,

$$\tau = \mu\dot\gamma,$$

we have precisely the constitutive equation of a viscous liquid as it is used in lubrication theory, and μ is the viscosity coefficient.

The behavior of viscoelastic materials is a mixture of the two simple cases described by (2.1) and (2.2) and by the models illustrated by Figures 2.1a and c. We shall now proceed to build up more complicated models by combining springs and dashpots, and to read from them possible patterns of viscoelastic behavior. Whether a given material performs according to one or another of these patterns is a question to be resolved by testing. If it does, we can apply our theory.

Since our models will be used to derive relations between stress and strain, all forces in springs and dashpots will be written as σ, and all extensions as ϵ.

2.2. Maxwell Fluid and Kelvin Solid

The first composite model to be studied is shown in Figure 2.2. The extension ϵ' of the spring follows from (2.1):

$$\sigma = E\epsilon', \tag{a}$$

while ϵ'' in the dashpot obeys the law (2.2):

$$\sigma = F\dot{\epsilon}''. \tag{b}$$

Since both elements are connected in series, the total elongation is

$$\epsilon = \epsilon' + \epsilon''. \tag{c}$$

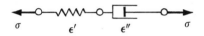

FIGURE 2.2. *Spring and dashpot in series: Maxwell material.*

We differentiate (a) and (c) and introduce $\dot{\epsilon}'$ and $\dot{\epsilon}''$ into (c) to find a relation between σ and ϵ, the force and the elongation of the spring-dashpot model:

$$\frac{\dot{\sigma}}{E} + \frac{\sigma}{F} = \dot{\epsilon}' + \dot{\epsilon}'' = \dot{\epsilon}.$$

This equation suggests that a similar relation might hold true as the constitutive relation of some viscoelastic material. We write it in the standard form

$$\sigma + p_1\dot{\sigma} = q_1\dot{\epsilon}. \tag{2.3}$$

To understand what this equation implies in terms of the behavior of a tension bar under load, we subject such a bar to a two-stage standard test.

In the first stage, we apply at $t = 0$ a constant stress $\sigma = \sigma_0$ and ask for $\epsilon(t)$. In this case, (2.3) is a differential equation for ϵ and has the solution

$$\epsilon = \frac{\sigma_0}{q_1}t + C_1, \qquad t > 0. \tag{2.4}$$

To find C_1, an initial condition is needed. The sudden application of the stress σ_0 at $t = 0$ means that $\dot{\sigma}(t)$ has a singularity at this point. To deal with it, we integrate (2.3) across this point:

$$\int_{-\tau}^{+\tau} \sigma\, dt + p_1[\sigma(+\tau) - \sigma(-\tau)] = q_1[\epsilon(+\tau) - \epsilon(-\tau)].$$

When $\tau \to 0$, the first term goes to zero and we are left with

$$p_1\sigma_0 = q_1\epsilon_0, \qquad \text{that is,} \qquad \epsilon_0 = \frac{p_1\sigma_0}{q_1} = \frac{\sigma_0}{E_0}, \tag{2.5}$$

where $\epsilon_0 = \epsilon(0^+)$ is the value of the ϵ immediately to the right of $t = 0$. When we now write (2.4) for $t = 0^+$ and introduce this value for ϵ, we find that

$$C_1 = \epsilon_0 = p_1\sigma_0/q_1,$$

and hence

$$\epsilon = \frac{\sigma_0}{q_1}(p_1 + t). \tag{2.6}$$

This result is represented in Figure 2.3 by the curves for $0 < t < t_1$.

In the second stage, which begins at $t = t_1$, the strain ϵ is fixed at whatever value ϵ_1 it has, that is, the ends of the test bar are fixed and we ask, what happens to the stress?

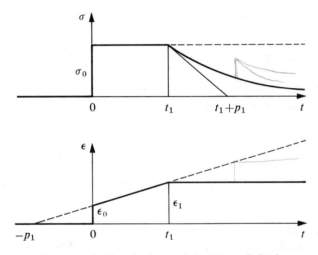

FIGURE 2.3. *Standard test of the Maxwell fluid.*

With $\epsilon = \epsilon_1$, $\dot{\epsilon} = 0$, (2.3) is a homogeneous differential equation for the stress σ and has the solution

$$\sigma = C_2\, e^{-t/p_1}, \qquad t > t_1. \tag{2.7}$$

To find C_2, we need $\sigma(t_1)$ or, more precisely, $\sigma(t_1^+)$, that is, the value which σ assumes just beyond a possible discontinuity. Any jump in the value of σ would mean an infinite value of $\dot{\sigma}$ and, from (2.3), an infinite $\dot{\epsilon}$. Since we see from Figure 2.3 that the strain rate is finite everywhere, we conclude that $\sigma(t^-) = \sigma(t^+)$ and hence $= \sigma_0$. Introducing this into (2.7), we find C_2 and then

$$\sigma = \sigma_0\, e^{-(t-t_1)/p_1}. \tag{2.8}$$

In the first stage, ϵ increases under constant stress. This phenomenon is called creep, and we shall speak of the *creep phase* of the test. In the second stage, the stress decreases under constant strain, that is, the material relaxes. This phase is called the *relaxation phase*.

In Figure 2.3, dotted lines indicate what would happen if the creep phase were to be extended beyond $t = t_1$. The strain would increase beyond all bounds. Physically speaking, this would, of course, soon lead us out of the domain of linear relations, and we would have to look for a more realistic representation of the actual behavior. Within the realm of the linear constitutive equation (2.3), however, the material shows a typical property of a fluid: its capability of unlimited deformation under finite stress. The material described by (2.3) and Figure 2.3 is therefore known as the *Maxwell fluid*. However, (2.5) shows that the response immediately after load application is elastic with a modulus E_0, the initial or impact modulus.

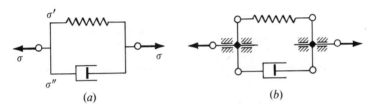

FIGURE 2.4. *Spring and dashpot parallel: Kelvin material.*

Another simple example is shown in Figure 2.4. While Figure 2.4a represents the usual way of displaying the model, it should be understood that the force σ is not to be distributed on the spring and the dashpot following the law of levers, but that really an arrangement is meant which is shown in more detail in Figure 2.4b. At all times the elongation ϵ of the two elements is the same, and the total force σ will be split into σ' (spring) and σ'' (dashpot) in whichever way it is necessary to make ϵ the same.

When applied to this model, (2.1) and (2.2) are

$$\sigma' = E\epsilon, \qquad \sigma'' = F\dot{\epsilon},$$

and from them we find

$$\sigma = \sigma' + \sigma'' = E\epsilon + F\dot{\epsilon},$$

which we write in the standard form

$$\sigma = q_0\epsilon + q_1\dot{\epsilon}. \tag{2.9}$$

Again, the constitutive equation is interpreted by performing the standard test.

When we let $\sigma = \sigma_0$, (2.9) has the solution

$$\epsilon = \frac{\sigma_0}{q_0} + C_1 e^{-\lambda t}, \qquad \lambda = \frac{q_0}{q_1}. \tag{2.10a, b}$$

When, at $t = 0$, σ jumps from 0 to σ_0, it remains finite and then (2.9) requires that $\dot{\epsilon}$ does the same. Therefore, ϵ cannot jump and the initial condition for (2.10a) is $\epsilon(0^+) = 0$. This leads to $C_1 = -\sigma_0/q_0$ and hence to

$$\epsilon = \frac{\sigma_0}{q_0}(1 - e^{-\lambda t}), \tag{2.11}$$

as illustrated by Figure 2.5. If, following the dotted lines, the creep phase is extended to $t \to \infty$, the strain does not grow indefinitely, but approaches the limit

$$\epsilon_\infty = \frac{\sigma_0}{q_0} = \frac{\sigma_0}{E_\infty}, \tag{2.12}$$

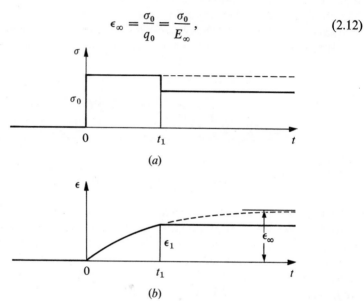

FIGURE 2.5. *Standard test of the Kelvin solid.*

which is proportional to the stress. This is almost the behavior of an elastic solid, the difference being that here the strain does not at once assume the final value, but approaches it gradually (delayed elasticity). The material represented by (2.9) and Figure 2.5 is therefore a solid and is known as the *Kelvin solid* or the *Voigt solid*. The quantity E_∞ is called the asymptotic modulus.

In the relaxation phase $t > t_1$ we keep $\epsilon = \epsilon_1$ and we find from (2.9) and (2.11)

$$\sigma = q_0\epsilon_1 = \sigma_0(1 - e^{-\lambda t_1}), \tag{2.13}$$

which is less than σ_0. When the strain is fixed, the stress is immediately relaxed by a certain amount and then remains forever at this value; that is, the relaxation is incomplete.

2.3.   Unit Step Function, Dirac Function, Laplace Transformation

So far we have described the sudden application of a stress σ by simply stating that $\sigma = 0$ for $t < 0$ and $\sigma = \sigma_0$ for $t > 0$, splitting the t axis in two parts, to which different stress formulas apply. There is a way of writing this in a more compact form and thus facilitating mathematical manipulation. The unit step function $\Delta(t)$ is defined by the two equations

$$\Delta(t) = 0 \quad \text{for} \quad t < 0, \quad \text{or } H(t) \qquad (2.14a)$$

$$\Delta(t) = 1 \quad \text{for} \quad t > 0. \qquad (2.14b)$$

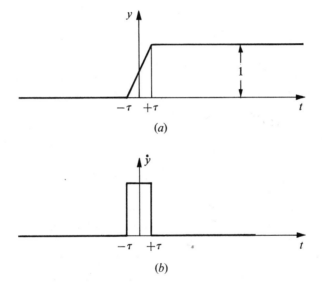

FIGURE 2.6.   *Derivation of* $\Delta(t)$ *and* $\delta(t)$.

For $t = 0$, the function is undefined unless we distinguish between $t = 0^-$ and $t = 0^+$ as the last point of negative time and the first point of positive time. With the help of this function, the creep phase is defined by putting $\sigma = \sigma_0 \, \Delta(t)$. In order to introduce this into differential equations, we need the time derivative of $\Delta(t)$. Figure 2.6 shows how $\Delta(t)$ may be conceived as the limiting case of a continuous function $y(t)$. It also shows the derivative $\dot{y}$, which equals zero except in a small interval around $t = 0$. The integral over any part of the t axis including this interval, that is, the area of the shaded rectangle, equals unity. If we let $\tau \to 0$, this rectangle will degenerate into a spike, infinitely thin and infinitely high, but still of unit area. It represents a highly singular function, $\delta(t)$, which is the derivative of $\Delta(t)$ and which may be defined by the following equations:

$$\delta(t) = 0 \qquad \text{for} \qquad t \neq 0, \tag{2.15a}$$

$$\delta(t) = +\infty \qquad \text{for} \qquad t = 0, \tag{2.15b}$$

$$\int_{-\infty}^{+\infty} \delta(t) \, dt = \int_{0^-}^{0^+} \delta(t) \, dt = 1. \tag{2.15c}$$

This function is known as the Dirac delta function.

After these preparations, let us return to Figure 2.5. We maintain the value of ϵ_1, but propose to reach the same strain in a shorter time, ultimately letting $t_1 \rightarrow 0$. We rewrite (2.11), using the series expansion of the exponential function:

$$\epsilon_1 = \frac{\sigma_0}{q_0}(1 - e^{-\lambda t_1}) = \frac{\sigma_0}{q_0}[1 - 1 + \lambda t_1 - \tfrac{1}{2}(\lambda t_1)^2 + - \cdots] = \frac{\sigma_0}{q_1} t_1 + \cdots .$$

We see that in the limit $\sigma_0 t_1 = \epsilon_1 q_1$, and that σ_0 must tend to infinity as t_1 tends to zero while the first part of Figure 2.5a degenerates into a Dirac spike $\sigma = \epsilon_1 q_1 \, \delta(t)$. Beyond the spike, (2.13) still holds true, and when we combine everything, we have

$$\sigma = \epsilon_1 q_1 \, \delta(t) + \epsilon_1 q_0 \, \Delta(t) \qquad \text{for} \qquad \epsilon = \epsilon_1 \Delta(t). \tag{2.16}$$

This equation represents the stress response of the Kelvin solid to an enforced sudden stretching. The Dirac part points to a high stress peak at the beginning. Such a peak occurs in all those materials that do not have an initial elastic response to a suddenly applied stress, that is, for which $E_0 = \infty$.

For our further operations a knowledge of the elements of the Laplace transformation will be necessary. For details beyond the brief introduction offered here the reader is referred to textbooks on the subject [4–9].

Take any function $f(t)$, such as stress or strain, and define its *Laplace transform*

$$\bar{f}(s) = \int_0^\infty f(t)e^{-st} \, dt. \tag{2.17}$$

Since we have integrated over t between fixed limits, $\bar{f}$ depends only on the rather meaningless variable s. The following facts are important:

(i). The values of $f(t)$ for $t < 0$ do not influence $\bar{f}(s)$.

(ii). The transforms of the derivatives of $f(t)$ have a simple relation to $\bar{f}(s)$.

To find this relation, we apply the transformation (2.17) to $\dot{f}(t)$ and integrate by parts:

$$\int_0^\infty \dot{f}(t)e^{-st} \, dt = [f(t)e^{-st}]_0^\infty - \int_0^\infty f(t)(-s)e^{-st} \, dt = -f(0) + s\bar{f}(s). \tag{2.18a}$$

Continuing this process, one easily verifies that

$$\int_0^\infty \ddot{f}(t)e^{-st}\,dt = -\dot{f}(0) - sf(0) + s^2\bar{f}(s), \tag{2.18b}$$

$$\int_0^\infty \dddot{f}(t)e^{-st}\,dt = -\ddot{f}(0) - s\dot{f}(0) - s^2f(0) + s^3\bar{f}(s). \tag{2.18c}$$

When $f(t)$ or its derivatives have a singularity at $t = 0$, it is necessary to choose between taking either 0^+ or 0^- as the lower limit of the integral in (2.17). In most cases we shall deal with functions which vanish for all $t < 0$, and when we then choose 0^- as a base, all the f terms in (2.18) vanish and

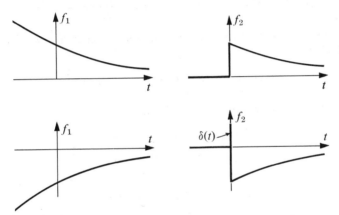

FIGURE 2.7. *Two interpretations of a function $f(t)$.*

the nth derivative of $f(t)$ has as its Laplace transform $s^n\bar{f}(s)$. The importance of the Laplace transformation as a tool for solving problems rests on the fact that a differentiation in the *physical plane* t, f is turned into an algebraic operation in the *Laplace plane* s, $\bar{f}$ and hence a differential equation is turned into an algebraic one, which is easier to solve. There is, however, the difficulty of transforming the solution $\bar{f}(s)$ back into the physical plane, that is, of finding the corresponding $f(t)$. The many methods needed to cope with this problem are one of the main subjects of books on the Laplace transformation.

As an example, consider the function $f(t) = e^{-\alpha t}$. From (2.17) we find

$$\bar{f}(s) = \int_0^\infty e^{-\alpha t}e^{-st}\,dt = -\frac{1}{\alpha + s}\,[e^{-(\alpha+s)t}]_0^\infty = \frac{1}{\alpha + s}\,.$$

Since the values of f for $t < 0$ do not enter the Laplace integral, we may identify $f(t)$ with either f_1 or f_2 shown in Figure 2.7. There is, however, a great difference in the derivatives of these functions. For f_1, (2.18a) yields the transform

$$\bar{f}_1'(s) = -1 + s\frac{1}{\alpha + s} = -\frac{\alpha}{\alpha + s},$$

but for f_2' it makes a difference whether 0^- or 0^+ is chosen as the lower limit in (2.17), since this means that the Dirac spike which corresponds to the jump in f_2 is either included or excluded. Based on 0^-, (2.18a) yields

$$\bar{f}_2'(s) = -f_2(0^-) + s\frac{1}{\alpha + s} = \frac{s}{\alpha + s},$$

but based on 0^+ it yields

$$\bar{f}_2'(s) = -f_2(0)^+ + s\frac{1}{\alpha + s} = -1 + \frac{s}{\alpha + s} = -\frac{\alpha}{\alpha + s}.$$

As another example we study the unit step function $f(t) = \Delta(t)$. In this case, (2.17) yields

$$\overline{\Delta}(s) = \int_{0^-}^{\infty} \Delta(t)e^{-st}\,dt = -\frac{1}{s}[e^{-st}]_0^{\infty} = \frac{1}{s}.$$

Based on 0^-, (2.18a) then yields the derivative

$$\bar{\delta}(s) = -\delta(0^-) + \frac{s}{s} = 1.$$

TABLE 2.1

Laplace Transform Pairs

	$f(t)$	$\bar{f}(s)$
(1)	$\Delta(t)$ or a constant	$1/s$
(2)	$\delta(t)$	1
(3)	$e^{-\alpha t}$	$1/(\alpha + s)$
(4)	$\dfrac{1}{\alpha}(1 - e^{-\alpha t})$	$1/s(\alpha + s)$
(5)	$\dfrac{t}{\alpha} - \dfrac{1}{\alpha^2}(1 - e^{-\alpha t})$	$1/s^2(\alpha + s)$
(6)	t^n	$n!\,s^{-n-1},\quad n = 0, 1, \ldots$
(7)*	$J_0(a\sqrt{t^2 - b^2}) \cdot \Delta(t - b)$	$\dfrac{1}{\sqrt{s^2 + a^2}}\exp(-b\sqrt{s^2 + a^2})$
(8)*	$2\sqrt{\dfrac{t}{\pi}}\exp\left(-\dfrac{n^2}{4t}\right) - n\left(1 - \operatorname{erf}\dfrac{n}{2\sqrt{t}}\right)$	$\dfrac{1}{s\sqrt{s}}\exp(-n\sqrt{s})$

* J_0 is the Bessel function, commonly denoted in this way, and erf is the error function.

The same result follows from direct integration:

$$\bar{\delta}(s) = \int_{0^-}^{\infty} \delta(t)e^{-st}\, dt = \int_{0^-}^{0^+} \delta(t)\, dt \cdot e^0 + \int_{0^+}^{\infty} 0 \cdot e^{-st}\, dt = 1.$$

These results and a few others have been compiled in Table 2.1. All entries in this table are based on 0^- and on the assumption that functions like $e^{-\alpha t}$ are interpreted like f_1 in Figure 2.7. More detailed tables may be found in [6]–[12] in the References.

2.4. Kelvin Chains and Maxwell Models

We now return to our subject of spring-dashpot models of viscoelastic materials. Figure 2.8 shows a spring and a Kelvin element in series. For the strains of both parts we have

$$\sigma = E\epsilon', \qquad \sigma = q_0''\epsilon'' + q_1''\dot{\epsilon}''.$$

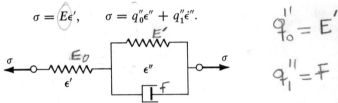

FIGURE 2.8. *Three-parameter solid.*

To both equations, the Laplace transformation is applied on both sides. Since E, q_0'', and q_1'' are constants, this yields

$$\bar{\sigma} = E\bar{\epsilon}', \qquad \bar{\sigma} = (q_0'' + s q_1'')\bar{\epsilon}''.$$

Multiplying each of these equations with a suitable constant and adding, we find

$$\bar{\sigma}(q_0'' + s q_1'') + E\bar{\sigma} = E(q_0'' + s q_1'')(\bar{\epsilon}' + \bar{\epsilon}'') = E(q_0'' + s q_1'')\bar{\epsilon},$$

where $\bar{\epsilon}$ is the transform of the total strain. Transforming back into the physical plane means removing bars and replacing every factor s by a differentiation:

$$(q_0'' + E)\sigma + q_1''\dot{\sigma} = E q_0''\epsilon + E q_1''\dot{\epsilon}.$$

This is written in the normalized form

$$\sigma + p_1\dot{\sigma} = q_0\epsilon + q_1\dot{\epsilon}. \tag{2.19}$$

Comparing the coefficients of both equations, one sees that

$$p_1 = q_1''/(E + q_0''), \qquad q_0 = E q_0''/(E + q_0''), \qquad q_1 = E q_1''/(E + q_0''),$$

and from these relations it follows that

$$\frac{q_1}{p_1} - q_0 = \frac{E^2}{E + q_0''}$$

is always positive, that is, that

$$q_1 > p_1 q_0. \tag{2.20}$$

If this inequality is not satisfied, it is not possible to derive (2.19) from the model, Figure 2.8, with real, positive values of the constants of its component parts. At present, it might appear that some other model could enable us to circumvent the inequality (2.20). We shall soon see, however, that this inequality is a physical necessity.

We explore the properties of the material by again subjecting it to the standard test. In the creep phase we have

$$\sigma = \sigma_0 \, \Delta(t), \qquad \bar{\sigma} = \sigma_0/s.$$

From the Laplace transform of (2.19) we have

$$\sigma_0 \left(\frac{1}{s} + p_1 \right) = (q_0 + q_1 s)\bar{\epsilon},$$

whence

$$\bar{\epsilon} = \sigma_0 \frac{1 + p_1 s}{s(q_0 + q_1 s)} = \frac{\sigma_0}{q_1} \left[\frac{1}{s(s + \lambda)} + \frac{p_1}{s + \lambda} \right]$$

with $\lambda = q_0/q_1$. In the last member of this equation, the function of s has been split into two parts which can readily be recognized in Table 2.1. Using this table backwards, we find the strain

$$\epsilon = \frac{\sigma_0}{q_1} \left[\frac{1}{\lambda} (1 - e^{-\lambda t}) + p_1 e^{-\lambda t} \right],$$

which may be written as

$$\epsilon = \frac{\sigma_0}{q_0} \left[1 - \left(1 - \frac{p_1 q_0}{q_1} \right) e^{-q_0 t / q_1} \right]. \tag{2.21}$$

Because of (2.20), the coefficient in parentheses is positive and $\epsilon(t)$ looks as shown in Figure 2.9. The material has instant elasticity with

$$\epsilon(0^+) = \epsilon_0 = \sigma_0 p_1/q_1 = \sigma_0/E_0$$

and also asymptotic elastic behavior,

$$\epsilon(\infty) = \epsilon_\infty = \sigma_0/q_0 = \sigma_0/E_\infty.$$

Therefore, it qualifies as a solid, the *three-parameter solid*. It is also known as the standard linear material. If (2.20) is violated, $\epsilon_\infty < \epsilon_0$, that is, a tension bar would, under sustained load, become gradually shorter!

For the relaxation phase, we shift our time scale and introduce a new time $\tau = t - t_1$. For $\tau \geq 0$ we may then write $\epsilon = \epsilon_1 \Delta(\tau)$, $\bar{\epsilon} = \epsilon_1/s$, and the Laplace transform of (2.19) then reads

$$\bar{\sigma} + p_1(s\bar{\sigma} - \sigma_0) = q_0 \bar{\epsilon} + q_1(s\bar{\epsilon} - \epsilon_1) = q_0 \epsilon_1/s.$$

Solving for $\bar{\sigma}$, we find

$$\bar{\sigma} = \frac{q_0 \epsilon_1}{s(1 + p_1 s)} + \frac{p_1 \sigma_0}{1 + p_1 s}.$$

Using the transformation pairs (3) and (4) of Table 2.1, we find from this the stress

$$\sigma = q_0 \epsilon_1 (1 - e^{-\tau/p_1}) + \sigma_0 e^{-\tau/p_1}. \tag{2.22}$$

This is the right half of the σ curve in Figure 2.9. The material relaxes gradually to $\sigma_\infty = q_0 \epsilon_1 = E_\infty \epsilon_1$. Note the meaning of $\lambda^{-1} = q_1/q_0$ and p_1 as abscissas

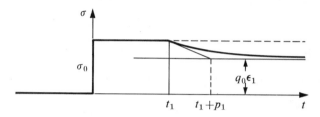

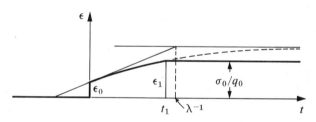

FIGURE 2.9. *Standard test of the three-parameter solid.*

of the intersections of initial tangents and asymptotes. Because of (2.20), $\lambda^{-1} > p_1$.

There are two ways of systematically building up more complicated models: the *Kelvin chain* and the *Maxwell model*. In the former (Figure 2.10a) an arbitrary number of different Kelvin units are connected in series, possibly including the degenerated units s and d. Presence of s leads to impact response ($E_0 \neq \infty$) and presence of d to fluid behavior ($E_\infty = 0$). In the Maxwell model, Maxwell units are connected in parallel (Figure 2.10b). In this case the absence of a degenerated unit d assures impact response and the absence of s leads to fluid behavior.

In Table 2.2 some models are shown with their differential equations and other information to be explained later.

$$\sigma + p_1 S\sigma = q_1 S\epsilon$$
$$\sigma(1 + p_1 S) = q_1 \epsilon$$

Model	Name	Differential equation _____ Inequalities	Creep compliance J(
	elastic solid	$\sigma = q_0\epsilon$	$1/q_0$
	viscous fluid	$\sigma = q_1\dot\epsilon$	t/q_1
	Maxwell fluid	$\sigma + p_1\dot\sigma = q_1\dot\epsilon$	$(p_1 + t)/q_1$
	Kelvin solid	$\sigma = q_0\epsilon + q_1\dot\epsilon$	$\dfrac{1}{q_0}(1 - e^{-\lambda t}), \qquad \lambda =$
	3-parameter solid _Standard_	$\sigma + p_1\dot\sigma = q_0\epsilon + q_1\dot\epsilon$ _____ $q_1 > p_1 q_0$	$\dfrac{p_1}{q_1}e^{-\lambda t} + \dfrac{1}{q_0}(1 - e^{-\lambda}$ $\lambda = q_0/q_1$
	3-parameter fluid _Zener_	$\sigma + p_1\dot\sigma = q_1\dot\epsilon + q_2\ddot\epsilon$ _____ $p_1 q_1 > q_2$	$\dfrac{t}{q_1} + \dfrac{p_1 q_1 - q_2}{q_1^2}(1 - $ $\lambda = q_1/q_2$
	4-parameter fluid _-Burger body_	$\sigma + p_1\dot\sigma + p_2\ddot\sigma = q_1\dot\epsilon + q_2\ddot\epsilon$ _____ $p_1 q_1 > q_2, \quad p_1^2 > 4p_2$ $p_1 q_1 q_2 > p_2 q_1^2 + q_2^2$	$\dfrac{t}{q_1} + \dfrac{p_1 q_1 - q_2}{q_1^2}(1 - $ $+ \dfrac{p_2}{q_2}e^{-\lambda t}, \quad \lambda = $
	4-parameter solid	$\sigma + p_1\dot\sigma = q_0\epsilon + q_1\dot\epsilon + q_2\ddot\epsilon$ _____ $q_1 > p_1 q_0, \quad q_1^2 > 4q_0 q_2$ $q_1 p_1 > q_0 p_1^2 + q_2$	$\dfrac{1 + p_1\lambda_1}{q_2\lambda_1(\lambda_2 - \lambda_1)}(1 - e^{-}$ $+ \dfrac{1 + p_1\lambda_2}{q_2\lambda_2(\lambda_1 - \lambda_2)}(1 - $ where λ_1, λ_2 are roc $q_2\lambda^2 - q_1\lambda + q_0 = $

16

$$\frac{\left(P_1+\frac{1}{S^2}\right)S^2}{q_1 S}\,S^2$$

Relaxation modulus $Y(t)$	Complex compliance	
	Real part $G_1(\omega)$	Imaginary part $G_2(\omega)$
q_0	$1/q_0$	0
$q_1\,\delta(t)$	$\dfrac{Gz-i}{e}=G-\dfrac{i}{z}$	$-1/q_1\omega$
$\dfrac{q_1}{p_1}e^{-t/p_1}\;\dfrac{1}{\left(S+\frac{1}{P_1}\right)}P_1$	$\dfrac{p_1}{q_1\omega}\;-i$	$\dfrac{z\omega-i}{(sz\,\omega)}\;-\dfrac{1}{q_1\omega}$
$q_0+q_1\,\delta(t)$	$\dfrac{q_0}{q_0^2+q_1^2\omega^2}$	$-\dfrac{q_1\omega}{q_0^2+q_1^2\omega^2}$
$\dfrac{q_1}{p_1}e^{-t/p_1}+q_0(1-e^{-t/p_1})$	$\dfrac{q_0+p_1q_1\omega^2}{q_0^2+q_1^2\omega^2}$	$-\dfrac{(q_1-q_0p_1)\omega}{q_0^2+q_1^2\omega^2}$
$\dfrac{q_2}{p_1}\,\delta(t)+\dfrac{1}{p_1}\left(q_1-\dfrac{q_2}{p_1}\right)e^{-t/p_1}$	$\dfrac{p_1q_1-q_2}{q_1^2+q_2^2\omega^2}$	$-\dfrac{q_1+p_1q_2\omega^2}{(q_1^2+q_2^2\omega^2)\omega}$
$\dfrac{1}{\sqrt{p_1^2-4p_2}}[(q_1-\alpha q_2)e^{-\alpha t}\\ -(q_1-\beta q_2)e^{-\beta t}],\\ \left.\begin{array}{c}\alpha\\\beta\end{array}\right\}=\dfrac{1}{2p_2}\left(p_1\pm\sqrt{p_1^2-4p_2}\right)$	$\dfrac{(p_1q_1-q_2)+p_2q_2\omega^2}{q_1^2+q_2^2\omega^2}$	$-\dfrac{q_1+(q_2p_1-p_2q_1)\omega^2}{(q_1^2+q_2^2\omega^2)\omega}$
$\dfrac{q_2}{p_1}\,\delta(t)+\dfrac{q_1p_1-q_2}{p_1^2}\\ -\dfrac{1}{p_1^2}(q_1p_1-q_0p_1^2-q_2)(1-e^{-t/p_1})$	$\dfrac{q_0+(p_1q_1-q_2)\omega^2}{q_0^2+(q_1^2-2q_0q_2)\omega^2+q_2^2\omega^4}$	$-\dfrac{(q_1-p_1q_0)\omega+q_2p_1\omega^3}{q_0^2+(q_1^2-2q_0q_2)\omega^2+q_2^2\omega^4}$

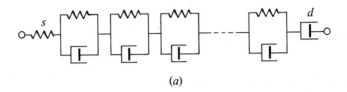

(a)

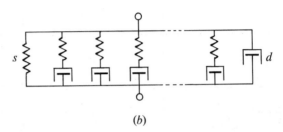

(b)

FIGURE 2.10. *Spring-dashpot models—a: Kelvin chain; b: Maxwell model.*

Obviously, the differential equation of any model of the Kelvin or Maxwell type has the form

$$\sigma + p_1\dot{\sigma} + p_2\ddot{\sigma} + \cdots = q_0\epsilon + q_1\dot{\epsilon} + q_2\ddot{\epsilon} + \cdots \qquad (2.23a)$$

or

$$\sum_0^m p_k \frac{d^k\sigma}{dt^k} = \sum_0^n q_k \frac{d^k\epsilon}{dt^k}. \qquad (2.23b)$$

Since we may divide the equation by a constant without changing its meaning, we shall always set $p_0 = 1$.

Equation (2.23b) may also be written as

$$\mathbf{P}\sigma = \mathbf{Q}\epsilon, \qquad (2.23c)$$

where $\mathbf{P}$ and $\mathbf{Q}$ are differential operators:

$$\mathbf{P} = \sum_0^m p_k \frac{d^k}{dt^k}, \qquad \mathbf{Q} = \sum_0^n q_k \frac{d^k}{dt^k}. \qquad (2.24a,b)$$

Each of these forms will be useful in our further studies.

When (2.23b) is subjected to the Laplace transformation, there results the following algebraic relation between the Laplace transforms $\bar{\sigma}(s)$ and $\bar{\epsilon}(s)$ of stress and strain:

$$\sum_0^m p_k s^k \bar{\sigma} = \sum_0^n q_k s^k \bar{\epsilon}. \qquad (2.25a)$$

It may be written in the form

$$\mathscr{P}(s)\cdot\bar{\sigma} = \mathscr{Q}(s)\cdot\bar{\epsilon}, \tag{2.25b}$$

in which $\mathscr{P}$ and $\mathscr{Q}$ are polynomials in s,

$$\mathscr{P}(s) = \sum_0^m p_k s^k, \qquad \mathscr{Q}(s) = \sum_0^n q_k s^k, \tag{2.26}$$

which have the same coefficients as the differential operators **P** and **Q**.

Table 2.3 is a systematic list of Kelvin chains of increasing length, showing the nonzero coefficients of the operators **P** and **Q** and the behavior of the

TABLE 2.3

Kelvin Chains

Model	Nonzero coefficients of **P**	Nonzero coefficients of **Q**	Number of parameters	E_0	Solid or fluid
s	p_0	q_0	1	E_0	solid
d	p_0	q_1	1	—	fluid
k	p_0	$q_0\ q_1$	2	—	solid
s-d	$p_0\ p_1$	q_1	2	E_0	fluid
s-k	$p_0\ p_1$	$q_0\ q_1$	3	E_0	solid
d-k	$p_0\ p_1$	$q_1\ q_2$	3	—	fluid
k-k	$p_0\ p_1$	$q_0\ q_1\ q_2$	4	—	solid
s-d-k	$p_0\ p_1\ p_2$	$q_1\ q_2$	4	E_0	fluid
s-k-k	$p_0\ p_1\ p_2$	$q_0\ q_1\ q_2$	5	E_0	solid
d-k-k	$p_0\ p_1\ p_2$	$q_1\ q_2\ q_3$	5	—	fluid
k-k-k	$p_0\ p_1\ p_2$	$q_0\ q_1\ q_2\ q_3$	6	—	solid
s-d-k-k	$p_0\ p_1\ p_2\ p_3$	$q_1\ q_2\ q_3$	6	E_0	fluid
s-k-k-k	$p_0\ p_1\ p_2\ p_3$	$q_0\ q_1\ q_2\ q_3$	7	E_0	solid

material for short and long time. In the first column the Kelvin chains are described by the spring (*s*), dashpot (*d*), and Kelvin units (*k*) they contain. In this notation the four-parameter fluid of Table 2.2 would be described by *s-k-d* or *s-d-k*. It may be seen from Table 2.3 that for every number of parameters there exists one solid and one fluid material and also one material with and one without initial elastic response.

Exercises

2.1. Verify the differential equations for the three last models in Table 2.2. If you are not familiar with the use of the Laplace transformation, you may write differential equations for the component parts and eliminate from them all those stresses or strains which cannot be measured at the terminals of the model. Verify also the inequalities.

2.2. Subject any of the three last models of Table 2.2 to the standard test.

2.3. For any one of the four last models, guess how the corresponding Maxwell model would look. Formulate its differential equation and check whether your guess was right.

2.4. Show that the four-parameter solid degenerates into the Kelvin material when its component parts are made equal.

2.5. Figure 2.11 shows a model which fits neither into the Kelvin nor into the Maxwell scheme. Derive its differential equation and the associated inequalities and show that the model represents the four-parameter solid.

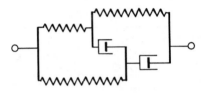

FIGURE 2.11.

2.6. For the three-parameter solid, express the constants p_1, q_0, q_1 in terms of the moduli of the two springs and the dashpot. Assume that the moduli of the springs are in the ratio of 10:1, the spring inside the Kelvin element having the lower modulus. Show that, for step loading, such a material behaves for some time almost like a Maxwell fluid, but ultimately turns out to be a solid.

REFERENCES

The following works are surveys of the field and may serve for collateral reading

[1] E. H. LEE, "Viscoelastic Stress Analysis. Structural Mechanics," in J. N. Goodier and N. J. Hoff (eds.), *Proceedings of the 1st Symposium on Naval Structural Mechanics, Stanford, 1958* (London: Pergamon, 1960), pp. 456–482.

[2] D. R. BLAND, *The Theory of Linear Viscoelasticity* (London: Pergamon, 1960). (Monograph on the subject contains many cases of stress analysis problems.)

Spring-dashpot models are studied in the following report:

[3] J. M. BURGERS, "Mechanical Considerations, Model Systems, Phenomenological Theories," in Akademie van Wetenschappen, *First Report on Viscosity and Plasticity* (Amsterdam: 1935), pp. 21–33.

The Laplace transformation is described in the following books, which should be consulted for depth and further detail:

[4] R. V. CHURCHILL, *Operational Mathematics* (2nd ed.) (New York: McGraw-Hill, 1958).

[5] W. T. Thomson, *Laplace Transformation* (2nd ed.) (Englewood Cliffs, N.J.: Prentice-Hall, 1960).

[6] H. S. Carslaw and J. C. Jaeger, *Operational Methods in Applied Mathematics* (2nd ed.) (Oxford: Oxford University Press, 1947; also New York: Dover Publications, 1963).

[7] E. J. Scott, *Transform Calculus with an Introduction to Complex Variables* (New York: Harper & Row, 1955).

[8] C. R. Wylie, *Advanced Engineering Mathematics* (2nd ed.) (New York: McGraw-Hill, 1960), Chap. 8.

[9] E. J. Scott, *Laplace Transformation*, in W. Flügge (ed.), *Handbook of Engineering Mechanics* (New York: McGraw-Hill, 1962), Chap. 19.

Tables of various size of Laplace transform pairs are contained in References [4] through [9], the largest among them with 125 entries in [4]. For farther going needs, the following tables may be used:

[10] A. Erdélyi, W. Magnus, F. Oberhettinger and F. Tricomi, *Tables of Integral Transforms* (New York: McGraw-Hill, 1954), Vol. 1, Chaps. 4 and 5.

[11] G. A. Campbell and R. M. Foster, *Fourier Integrals for Practical Applications* (Princeton, N.J.: D. Van Nostrand, 1948). (With proper precautions, this table may be used for Laplace transforms. It is easy to use and contains much material.)

[12] W. Magnus and F. Oberhettinger, *Formeln und Sätze für die speziellen Funktionen der mathematischen Physik* (Berlin: Springer-Verlag, 1943) pp. 122–136. (Part of a book containing much additional information about some of the exotic functions occurring as inverses of simple Laplace transforms.)

[13] G. Doetsch, *Tabellen zur Laplace-Transformation* (Berlin: Springer-Verlag, 1947).

CHAPTER 3

Hereditary Integrals

$\mathrm{T}_{\text{HUS FAR}}$, we have described viscoelastic materials by their differential equations. We shall now learn to describe them by another means, the hereditary integrals. Each of them can express all the facts contained in the differential equation (2.23) and even has the advantage of greater flexibility when it comes to rendering the measured properties of an actual material.

3.1. Creep Compliance, Relaxation Modulus

To study the behavior of viscoelastic models, we have used a standard test consisting of a creep phase and a relaxation phase. In the creep phase we applied a stress $\sigma = \sigma_0 \Delta(t)$ and calculated the time-dependent strain ϵ. Since we are considering only linear materials, the strain is always proportional to σ_0 and may be written as

$$\epsilon(t) = \sigma_0 J(t). \qquad (3.1)$$

The function $J(t)$ is the strain per unit of applied stress, and is different for each material. It describes, in a certain way, its stress-strain behavior, and we shall see soon that it describes it completely. For $t < 0$, $J(t) \equiv 0$, and since, under sustained load, a tension bar will never get shorter, $J(t)$ is for $t > 0$ a monotonically increasing function. It is called the *creep compliance*. In Table 2.2 it is listed for those materials which can be represented by simple models.

To obtain $J(t)$ from the differential equation of a material, we let $\sigma = \Delta(t)$ and $\epsilon = J(t)$, and solve for the latter with the initial condition that ϵ and all its derivatives (as far as needed) vanish for $t = 0^-$. This is most conveniently done with the help of the Laplace transformation, that is, by introducing $\bar{\sigma}(s) = s^{-1}$ in (2.25b) and solving it for $\bar{\epsilon} = \bar{J}(s)$. This yields

$$\bar{J}(s) = \frac{\mathscr{P}(s)}{s\,\mathscr{Q}(s)}. \tag{3.2}$$

The result is transformed back into the physical plane to yield $J(t)$. Since the quotient of two polynomials can always be split into partial fractions, the transformation pairs of Table 2.1 are sufficiently extensive in scope and $J(t)$ always appears as a sum of exponentials plus, possibly, a linear term.

As an example, take a Kelvin model consisting of three Kelvin units in series, as shown in Figure 2.10a, but without the spring s and the dashpot d. It represents a solid and does not show impact response. Its differential equation must contain six parameters, among them q_0, and therefore must be

$$\sigma + p_1\dot{\sigma} + p_2\ddot{\sigma} = q_0\epsilon + q_1\dot{\epsilon} + q_2\ddot{\epsilon} + q_3\dddot{\epsilon},$$

which is in agreement with the entry in Table 2.3. From (3.2) we find

$$\bar{J}(s) = \frac{1 + p_1 s + p_2 s^2}{s(q_0 + q_1 s + q_2 s^2 + q_3 s^3)}$$

This may be split into partial fractions if the roots of the denominator are known. Let

$$q_0 + q_1 s + q_2 s^2 + q_3 s^3 = q_3(s - \lambda_1)(s - \lambda_2)(s - \lambda_3),$$

then

$$\bar{J}(s) = \frac{1}{q_3}\frac{1}{s}\left(\frac{a_1}{s - \lambda_1} + \frac{a_2}{s - \lambda_2} + \frac{a_3}{s - \lambda_3}\right),$$

where

$$a_1 = \frac{1 + p_1\lambda_1 + p_2\lambda_1^2}{(\lambda_1 - \lambda_2)(\lambda_1 - \lambda_3)}, \quad \text{etc.}$$

Using the transform pair (4) of Table 2.1, one finds

$$J(t) = \frac{1}{q_3}\sum_{n=1}^{3}\frac{a_n}{-\lambda_n}(1 - e^{\lambda_n t}).$$

Obviously, the exponentials must be decreasing functions of time, and this requires that λ_1, λ_2, $\lambda_3 < 0$. One of the inequalities that can be found by a detailed analysis of the model guarantees that this is the case.

We may invert the procedure which led to $J(t)$, prescribing $\epsilon = \epsilon_0\,\Delta(t)$ and asking for the corresponding stress. This amounts to applying at $t = 0$ whatever stress is needed (possibly even a Dirac spike) to produce the desired extension, then fixing the terminals of the model or the ends of the tension bar and watching what stress will develop. Since the equations are linear, σ will be proportional to ϵ_0:

$$\sigma(t) = \epsilon_0 Y(t). \tag{3.3}$$

The function $Y(t)$ is called the *relaxation modulus* and is always a monotonically decreasing or, at least, a nonincreasing function of time. Letting $\bar{\epsilon} = s^{-1}$ and $\bar{\sigma} = \overline{Y}(s)$ in (2.25b) leads to

$$\overline{Y}(s) = \frac{\mathscr{Q}(s)}{s\,\mathscr{P}(s)}, \tag{3.4}$$

from which $Y(t)$ may be found.

The relaxation modulus and the creep compliance are connected by a simple relation between their Laplace transforms, which results from a comparison of (3.2) and (3.4):

$$\bar{J}(s)\,\overline{Y}(s) = s^{-2}. \tag{3.5}$$

Formulas for the relaxation moduli of simple materials have been listed in Table 2.2. As may be seen there, $Y(t)$ contains a Dirac function if the material is lacking impact response. This is quite understandable, because if a finite stress is not sufficient to produce at once a finite strain, an infinite one will be needed.

It should be noted that by their very definition both $J(t)$ and $Y(t)$ are zero for all $t < 0$, and that the formulas given in Table 2.2 are therefore applicable only for $t > 0$.

3.2. Hereditary Integrals

Since all our materials are linear, we may use the rule of linear superposition to calculate the strain produced by the common action of several loads. For the tension bars considered thus far, "several loads" cannot mean anything but tensile stresses of different magnitudes applied successively. As an example, consider the case shown in Figure 3.1. At $t = 0$ a stress σ_0 is applied suddenly, which produces a strain $\epsilon = \sigma_0 J(t)$. If the stress σ_0 is maintained unchanged, this equation will describe the strain for the entire future; but if, at $t = t'$, some more stress is added, then for $t > t'$ additional strain will be produced which is proportional to $\Delta\sigma'$ and which depends on the same creep compliance. However, for this additional strain, time is measured by a clock that starts running at $t = t'$. The total strain for $t > t'$ is, therefore,

$$\epsilon(t) = \sigma_0 J(t) + \Delta\sigma' J(t - t').$$

From this equation it is but one step to a very general case. Assume that, as before, a stress σ_0 is suddenly applied at $t = 0$, but that σ then varies as an arbitrary function $\sigma(t)$. As shown in Figure 3.2, this stress diagram can be broken up into the basic part $\sigma_0 \Delta(t)$ and a sequence of infinitesimal step functions $d\sigma' \cdot \Delta(t - t')$ where $d\sigma' = (d\sigma/dt)_{t=t'} dt'$, which we shall write as $(d\sigma'/dt') dt'$. The corresponding strain at time t is then the sum of the strain

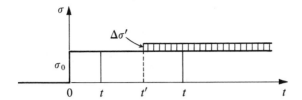

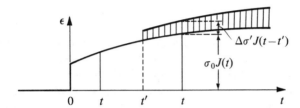

FIGURE 3.1. *Linear superposition of step inputs.*

caused by all the steps that have taken place at times $t' < t$, that is,

$$\epsilon(t) = \sigma_0 J(t) + \int_0^t J(t - t') \frac{d\sigma'}{dt'} \, dt'. \tag{3.6a}$$

This formula shows how the strain at any given time depends on all that has happened before—on the entire *stress history* $\sigma'(t')$, $t' < t$. This is quite different from what happens in an elastic material, whose strain depends at any time solely on the stress acting at that time only.

The integral in (3.6a) is called a *hereditary integral*. Through integration by parts it may be brought into another, often useful form:

$$\epsilon(t) = \sigma_0 J(t) + [J(t - t') \cdot \sigma(t')]_0^t - \int_0^t \sigma(t') \frac{dJ(t - t')}{dt'} \, dt'.$$

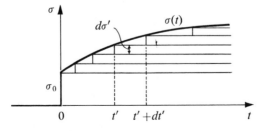

FIGURE 3.2. *Derivation of the hereditary integral.*

It should be noted that all the zeros in these equations mean 0^+. Therefore, when the bracketed boundary term is evaluated, it combines with the first term. On the other hand, we may write $dJ(t - t')/dt' = -dJ(t - t')/d(t - t')$ and thus arrive at the following, second version of the hereditary integral:

$$\epsilon(t) = \sigma(t)J(0) + \int_0^t \sigma(t') \frac{dJ(t - t')}{d(t - t')} \, dt'. \tag{3.6b}$$

While (3.6a) separates the strains caused by the initial load σ_0 and by later load increases, (3.6b) shows the strain that would occur if the total stress σ were applied right now at t, and the additional strain stemming from the fact that much or all of the stress has been applied earlier and has had time to produce some creep.

The hereditary integral (3.6a) may be subjected to some formal changes which, at times, make it easier to use. First, since $J(t) = 0$ for all $t < 0$, it does not make any difference if the upper limit of the integral is raised above $t' = t$, even to $t' = \infty$, since in the added integration interval $J(t - t')$ has a negative argument. If this change is made in the upper limit, it must, of course, not be forgotten that any analytic expressions for $J(t)$—for example, those listed in Table 2.2—are not valid for negative arguments.

Another formal change may be made as follows: Instead of $(d\sigma'/dt') \, dt'$ we may simply write $d\sigma'$ or $d\sigma(t')$ and integrate over all increments of stress, using with each one the proper time t' in the argument of $J(t - t')$. It then makes no difference when many increments $d\sigma'$ occur in rapid succession or even all at the same time, adding up to a finite step $\Delta\sigma_1$ at some time $t = t_1$. We may then also absorb the initial step σ_0 into the integral, and even move its lower limit to $t' = -\infty$, since for $t' < 0$ there is no $\sigma(t')$ and hence no contribution to the integral. In this way we arrive at the following form of the hereditary integral:

$$\epsilon(t) = \int_{t'=-\infty}^{t'=+\infty} J(t - t') \, d\sigma(t'). \tag{3.6c}$$

Integrals of this form are known as *Stieltjes integrals*.

As an example, we may consider the stress history of Figure 3.3. With $\sigma_0 = 0$ and $\sigma = \sigma_1 t/t_1$ we find from (3.6b) for a Maxwell material in the range $t < t_1$:

$$\epsilon(t) = \frac{\sigma_1 t}{t_1} \cdot \frac{p_1}{q_1} + \frac{\sigma_1}{t_1} \int_0^t t' \cdot \frac{1}{q_1} \, dt' = \frac{\sigma_1}{q_1 t_1} \left(p_1 t + \frac{t^2}{2} \right).$$

For $t > t_1$, the integral must be broken into two parts:

$$\epsilon(t) = \sigma_1 \cdot \frac{p_1}{q_1} + \frac{\sigma_1}{t_1} \int_0^{t_1} t' \cdot \frac{1}{q_1} \, dt' + \sigma_1 \int_{t_1}^t \frac{1}{q_1} \, dt' = \frac{\sigma_1}{q_1} \left(p_1 - \frac{t_1}{2} + t \right).$$

If the total stress σ_1 had been applied suddenly at $t = t_1$, the strain would be

$$\epsilon(t) = \sigma_1 J(t - t_1) = \frac{\sigma_1}{q_1}(p_1 + t - t_1),$$

which is less, and if the load had been applied all at once at $t = 0$, we would have

$$\epsilon(t) = \sigma_1 J(t) = \frac{\sigma_1}{q_1}(p_1 + t),$$

which is more. The differences between these three load histories will be felt undiminished no matter how much time elapses.

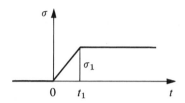

FIGURE 3.3. *Stress history.*

A quite different result is found for the Kelvin material. With $\sigma(t)$ from Figure 3.3, we then have for $t > t_1$:

$$\epsilon(t) = \frac{\sigma_1}{t_1 q_1}\int_0^{t_1} t' e^{-q_0(t-t')/q_1}\,dt' + \frac{\sigma_1}{q_1}\int_{t_1}^t e^{-q_0(t-t')/q_1}\,dt'$$

$$= \frac{\sigma_1}{q_0}\left[1 + \frac{q_1}{q_0 t_1}(1 - e^{q_0 t_1/q_1})e^{-q_0 t/q_1}\right].$$

For $t \to \infty$, this goes to $\epsilon = \sigma_1/q_0$, and the same limit would be approached if σ_1 were to be applied suddenly at $t = t_1$ or at $t = 0$, that is, the differences of stress history are wiped out if enough time has elapsed. The two examples show the typical difference between fluid and solid behavior.

The hereditary integrals (3.6a–c) have been derived from the definition of the creep compliance contained in (3.1). A similar argument may start from the concept of the relaxation modulus $Y(t)$ in (3.3). If the strain of a tension bar is known as a function of time (*strain history*) the stress follows from

$$\sigma(t) = \epsilon_0 Y(t) + \int_0^t Y(t - t')\frac{d\epsilon'}{dt'}\,dt' \tag{3.7a}$$

$$= \epsilon(t)Y(0) + \int_0^t \epsilon(t')\frac{dY(t - t')}{d(t - t')}\,dt' \tag{3.7b}$$

$$= \int_{t'=-\infty}^{t'=+\infty} Y(t - t')\,d\epsilon(t'). \tag{3.7c}$$

The following example illustrates the use of (3.7a–c). The ends of a tension

bar made of a Maxwell material are moved so as to produce the strain
history shown in Figure 3.4a. To calculate the ensuing stress, we apply
(3.7b). The term before the integral is either $= \epsilon_0 q_1/p_1$ or $= 0$, depending on
whether the bar is stretched or not. At $t = (2nt_1)^-$, that is, immediately
before a new cycle of stretching and unstretching begins, the integral yields

$$\sigma = \sum_{v=0}^{n-1} \int_{2vt_1}^{(2v+1)t_1} \frac{-q_1\epsilon_0}{p_1^2} \exp\left(-(2nt_1 - t')/p_1\right) dt'.$$

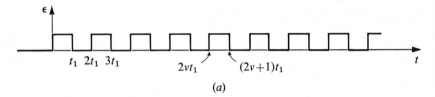

(a)

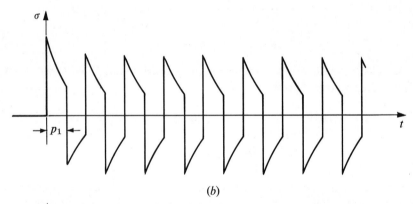

(b)

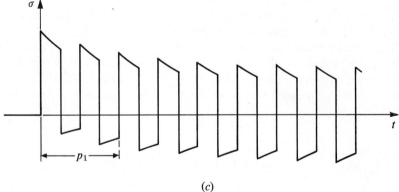

(c)

FIGURE 3.4. *Maxwell material—a: prescribed strain history; b, c: stress
histories for $t_1/p_1 = 1.0$ and 0.25, respectively.*

which may be evaluated by first performing the integration and then summing a geometric series. The result is

$$\sigma = - \frac{\epsilon_0 q_1}{p_1} \frac{1 - e^{-2nt_1/p_1}}{1 + e^{t_1/p_1}} .$$

Similarly, (3.7b) may be evaluated for other points t within each cycle. The result is shown in Figure 3.4b and c for two choices of t_1 in terms of the relaxation time p_1 of the material. One sees how the bar adjusts itself to a system of alternating positive and negative stresses of the same magnitude. If $t_1 = p_1$, the steady state has almost been reached after four cycles, while for $t_1 = 0.25p_1$ more cycles are needed.

3.3. Integral Equations

The differential equation (2.23) describes a viscoelastic material completely. If the stress history $\sigma(t)$ is known, we may solve (2.23) for $\epsilon(t)$, and if the strain history is known, we may use the same equation to find the stress.

We shall now see that each of the hereditary integrals (3.6) and (3.7), taken alone, can do the same service. Let us assume that $\sigma(t)$ is known. Then (3.6b) obviously leads to $\epsilon(t)$, and we used it in this way when we calculated the strain produced by the stress history of Figure 3.3. Now let $\epsilon(t)$ be known and $\sigma(t)$ be unknown. Then (3.6b) has the form

$$\sigma(t) + \int_0^t \sigma(t')K(t, t') \, dt' = f(t), \qquad (3.8)$$

where $f(t) = \epsilon(t)/J(0)$ and the *kernel*

$$K(t, t') = \frac{1}{J(0)} \frac{dJ(t - t')}{d(t - t')}$$

are known functions of their arguments. Equation (3.8) is called an *integral equation*, more precisely, an integral equation of the second kind of the Volterra type*. It has a unique solution and thus determines the stress when the strain is known. We shall later repeatedly encounter Volterra's integral equation, and then learn more about it. At present it suffices to know that knowledge of one function, $J(t)$, through the double use of (3.6), permits finding ϵ from σ and σ from ϵ, that is, that this function describes the material as completely as does the differential equation (2.23). The same statement applies to the relaxation modulus $Y(t)$, since the hereditary integral (3.7) can be used "forward" to find $\sigma(t)$ from $\epsilon(t)$ and "backward," that is, as an integral equation, to find ϵ from σ.

---

* In an integral equation of the first kind the term $\sigma(t)$ outside the integral is missing. In the Volterra type the upper limit of the integral is the independent variable t.

Exercises

3.1. The right end A of a Scotch yoke mechanism (Figure 3.5) has the horizontal displacement $r \sin \omega t$. At $t = 0$ it makes contact for the first time with the left end B of the viscoelastic bar BC. Find the stress in the bar as a function of time. At what time do the points A and B cease to be in contact? What happens next? Continue the investigation to cover many periods of the motion of the yoke. The problem may be solved in general terms or for a Maxwell or Kelvin material.

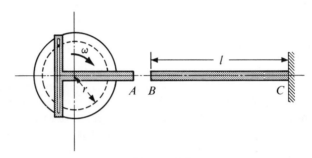

FIGURE 3.5.

3.2. A viscoelastic material is represented by a chain of three Kelvin elements. Let q be a reference constant of the dimension of a stress and T a reference time, and assume the following viscoelastic coefficients for the Kelvin elements: first element: $q_0 = 2q, q_1 = 2qT$; second element: $q_0 = q, q_1 = 4qT$; third element: $q_0 = 1.5q$, $q_1 = 16.5qT$. Find $\bar{J}(s)$ and from it $J(t)$. Then calculate and plot $\epsilon(t)$ for the following two stress histories:

$$(i). \quad \sigma = \sigma_0[\Delta(t) - \Delta(t - 0.8T)].$$

$$(ii). \quad \sigma = \sigma_0[\Delta(t) - \Delta(t - 3T)].$$

Study on the graphs to which extent the different Kelvin elements get into action.

3.3. For the same material as in the preceding exercise, find $\bar{Y}(s)$ and then $Y(t)$. Is the material solid or fluid? Does it have impact response?

REFERENCES

Hereditary integrals are discussed to some extent in most of the references given in Chapter 2; see [1], p. 462. See also the following handbook article:

[14] E. H. Lee, "Viscoelasticity," in W. Flügge (ed.), *Handbook of Engineering Mechanics* (New York: McGraw-Hill, 1962), Chap. 53, pp. 8–9.

The following sources may be consulted for integral equations. They will be useful to readers who wish to go beyond the few simple facts needed for the understanding of this book:

[15] W. V. LOVITT, *Linear Integral Equations* (New York: Dover Publications, 1950).

[16] F. B. HILDEBRAND, *Methods of Applied Mathematics* (Englewood Cliffs, N.J.: Prentice-Hall, 1952), Chap. 4.

[17] M. A. HEASLET, "Integral equations," in W. Flügge (ed.), *Handbook of Engineering Mechanics*, (New York: McGraw-Hill, 1962), Chap. 17.

CHAPTER 4

Viscoelastic Beams

W<small>E ARE NOW</small> prepared to solve some simple stress problems involving a viscoelastic material. The subject of our study will be a structure, that is, a deformable body of known shape to which external forces, the loads, are applied. We shall use the term "structure" to cover anything, as simple as a tension bar or as complicated as an entire bridge or an entire airplane. The structures to be considered in this chapter are straight beams of constant cross section, but the results obtained apply to any structure in uni-axial stress.

4.1. The Correspondence Principle

For any structure the general problem of stress analysis is this: Given the dimensions and the material of the structure and a set of loads applied to it, what are the stresses in it and how will it be deformed? Very often only part of the complete problem is solved. In many cases only the stresses are of interest and the deformation is either not asked for at all or is investigated only to the extent that it influences the stress distribution, as for example in statically indeterminate structures.

The general problem is the same for elastic and for viscoelastic structures. In both cases the three basic sets of equations must be satisfied; the equilibrium conditions, the kinematic relations, and the constitutive equations, as explained on p. 2, the only difference being that for viscoelastic structures Hooke's law is to be replaced by another equation.

Since we have, so far, formulated the viscoelastic law only for the case of uni-axial tension or compression, we must restrict here our attention to structures in which only uni-axial stress occurs. Besides simple tension and compression members, these are trusses and beams. For these the constitutive equation is a single relation between the stress σ and the strain ϵ, and we may choose either the differential equation (2.23) or one of the hereditary integrals (3.6) or (3.7).

Obviously, we could easily extend the scope of our operations to the torsion of prismatic bars and of circular shafts of variable diameter [18], since in these cases the stress system consists at each point of one pair of shear stresses τ_{ij} and for these and the corresponding shear strain γ_{ij} we might write a constitutive equation of the same kind. Of course, the numerical values of the coefficients p_k, q_k and the functions $J(t)$ and $Y(t)$ would be different. This chapter, however, will be restricted to the study of beams.

Consider first an elastic beam carrying certain loads P_i, $i = 1, 2, \ldots$. There are bending stresses $\sigma(x, y, z)$ that satisfy the equilibrium conditions for every element of the beam. Then there are strains $\epsilon(x, y, z)$, which (i) are connected with the stresses by Hooke's law

$$\epsilon(x, y, z) = \sigma(x, y, z)/E$$

and which (ii) are so distributed that plane cross sections remain plane and that the beam curvature calculated from them yields, after two integrations, a deflection $w(x)$ that satisfies all support conditions.

Now consider a beam of the same shape, but made of a viscoelastic material. Assume that the same loads are applied to it at $t = 0$ and then held constant, that is, that the beam carries the loads

$$P_i(t) = P_i \, \Delta(t).$$

Consider as a tentative solution of its stress problem the time-dependent stresses

$$\sigma(x, y, z; t) = \sigma(x, y, z) \, \Delta(t),$$

where σ on the right-hand side is the stress in the elastic beam. In the viscoelastic material there would then be strains

$$\epsilon(x, y, z; t) = \sigma(x, y, z)J(t).$$

At any time t they would be distributed like the strains in an elastic beam of modulus $E = 1/J(t)$, and hence they would satisfy all the kinematic conditions of the problem. From this we conclude that our tentative solution is the correct solution for the viscoelastic beam, and we have the following first version of the *correspondence principle*: If a viscoelastic beam is subjected to loads which are all applied simultaneously at $t = 0$ and then held constant, its stresses are the same as those in an elastic beam under the same load, and its strains and displacements depend on time and are derived from those of the elastic problem by replacing E by $1/J(t)$.

Now let us turn to a beam problem in which not the loads but the displacements of selected points are prescribed. As an example, we might think of a cantilever beam whose free end is suddenly deflected by a certain amount w_0 and then held in this position. For a tentative solution, we start from the deflections $w(x)$ of the elastic beam. Through certain kinematic relations they are connected with strains $\epsilon(x, y, z)$ and through Hooke's law with stresses $\sigma(x, y, z)$, which satisfy all equilibrium conditions. If we adopt for the viscoelastic beam deflections $w(x, t) = w(x) \cdot \Delta(t)$ and strains

$$\epsilon(x, y, z; t) = \epsilon(x, y, z) \Delta(t),$$

they will satisfy the kinematic conditions and also our boundary condition prescribing the displacement $w_0 \cdot \Delta(t)$ at the end. In the viscoelastic beam these strains would be accompanied by stresses

$$\sigma(x, y, z; t) = \epsilon(x, y, z) Y(t)$$

which, being proportional to the elastic stresses, would satisfy the same zero-load equilibrium conditions and hence would be acceptable for the

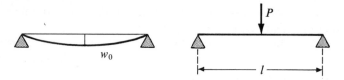

FIGURE 4.1. *Viscoelastic beam with prescribed deflection w_0.*

viscoelastic beam. This leads us to the second version of the *correspondence principle*: If a viscoelastic beam is subjected to forced displacements of certain points, which are all imposed at $t = 0$ and then held constant, the displacements of all points and all the strains are the same as in the corresponding elastic beam, and the stresses are derived from those of the elastic problem by multiplying them by $Y(t)/E$.

Both forms of the correspondence principle apply in the same form to trusses and to beam structures like portal frames and arches. They may be extended to the torsion problem mentioned before if E is replaced by the shear modulus G, and $J(t)$ and $Y(t)$ are replaced by the shear creep compliance and the shear relaxation modulus.

As an example consider the beam shown in Figure 4.1. It is originally straight, and at $t = 0$ a deflection w_0 is forced upon its midspan point. To do this, a still unknown force P is needed. For an elastic beam we may find in any handbook the relation

$$w_0 = \frac{Pl^3}{48EI}.$$

We solve for P and replace E by the relaxation modulus to find

$$P = \frac{48Iw_0}{l^3} Y(t).$$

Using formulas from Table 2.2, the results plotted in Figure 4.2 may be obtained.

If the beam material is a three-parameter solid, the force needed to hold the beam is less than the one for first pushing it down, both being connected by a gradual transition.

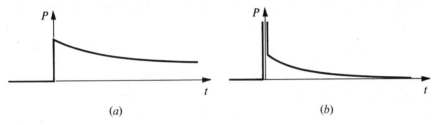

(a)   (b)

FIGURE 4.2. *Force P needed for the beam in Figure 4.1—a: three-parameter solid; b: three-parameter fluid.*

The three-parameter fluid does not at once deform under a finite load, and a Dirac spike

$$P = \frac{48Iw_0}{l^3} \frac{q_1}{p_1} \delta(t)$$

is needed to make the beam deflect; but after a length of time the force needed to hold it down relaxes and tends to zero. The beam "gets used" to being bent and will not spring back when released if it has been held down long enough.

4.2. Hereditary Integrals

Let $w(x)$ be the deflection of a beam under a load $p(x)$, assuming an elastic material of modulus $E = 1$. Then, because of the correspondence principle,

$$w(x, t) = w(x)J(t)$$

is the deflection for the same beam, but made of a viscoelastic material and subjected to the step function load $p(x, t) = p(x) \cdot \Delta(t)$. We may easily generalize this statement to an arbitrary load history

$$p(x, t) = p(x)f(t)$$

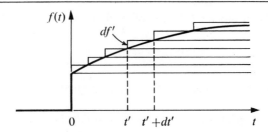

FIGURE 4.3. *Hereditary integral for beams.*

by breaking it down into a sequence of infinitesimal steps as shown in Figure 4.3. We have then

$$w(x, t) = \mathfrak{w}(x)\left[f(0^+) \cdot J(t) + \int_{0^+}^{t} J(t - t') \frac{df(t')}{dt'} \, dt' \right], \qquad (4.1a)$$

which is the same hereditary integral as (3.6a). Integration by parts will bring it again into the form

$$w(x, t) = \mathfrak{w}(x)\left[f(t)J(0^+) + \int_{0^+}^{t} f(t') \frac{dJ(t - t')}{d(t - t')} \, dt' \right], \qquad (4.1b)$$

and a form corresponding to (3.6c) is also possible.

As an example, consider a beam carrying a uniform load p, but with one of the histories shown in Figure 4.4b and c. The elastic deflection with $E = 1$ is

$$\mathfrak{w}(x) = \frac{16\mathfrak{w}_0}{5l^4} (x^4 - 2lx^3 + l^3x),$$

where

$$\mathfrak{w}_0 = \frac{5\bar{p}l^4}{384I}$$

is the midspan deflection. For the load history of Figure 4.4b we find from (4.1a) for $0 < t < t_1$:

$$w(\tfrac{1}{2}l, t) = \frac{5\bar{p}l^4}{384It_1} \int_{0^+}^{t} J(t - t') \, dt'$$

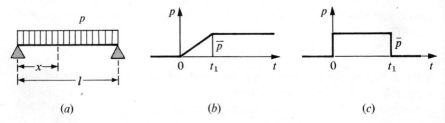

FIGURE 4.4. *Beam with two load histories.*

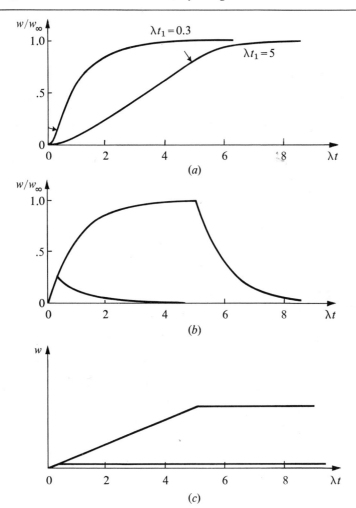

FIGURE 4.5. *Deflection of the beam shown in Figure* 4.4a—*a: load history of Figure* 4.3b, *Kelvin material; b, c: load history of Figure* 4.3c, *Kelvin and Maxwell materials.*

and for $t > t_1$:

$$w(\tfrac{1}{2}l, t) = \frac{5\bar{p}l^4}{384It_1} \int_{0^+}^{t_1} J(t - t') \, dt'.$$

For a Kelvin material, evaluation of the integrals yields the following formulas, which lead to the curves shown in Figure 4.5a:

for $0 < t < t_1$:

$$w(\tfrac{1}{2}l, t) = \frac{5\bar{p}l^4}{384Iq_0 t_1}\left[t - \frac{q_1}{q_0}(1 - e^{-\lambda t})\right],$$

and for $t > t_1$:

$$w(\tfrac{1}{2}l, t) = \frac{5\bar{p}l^4}{384 I q_0 t_1}\left[t_1 - \frac{q_1}{q_0}(e^{\lambda t_1} - 1)e^{-\lambda t}\right].$$

The two curves represent extreme cases. The time $\lambda^{-1} = q_1/q_0$ is characteristic for the creep of the material. It is the time at which the initial tangent to the creep curve in Figure 2.5b reaches the asymptote $\epsilon = \epsilon_\infty$. If $\lambda t_1 = 0.3$, the time t_1 needed for applying the full load $\bar{p}$ is only a fraction of λ^{-1}, and therefore not much deformation takes place during this time. Of the ultimate deflection, 86% comes from creep under full load. The behavior of the beam approaches the case of sudden loading. The second curve in Figure 4.5a belongs to a load that is very gently applied. After a short transient the deflection increases almost linear with the load, reaching 80% of its ultimate value when the loading is accomplished.

Now to the load history of Figure 4.4c. In this case we use (4.1b) and find for $0 < t < t_1$:

$$w(\tfrac{1}{2}l, t) = \frac{5\bar{p}l^4}{384 I}\left[J(0) + \int_0^t \frac{dJ(t - t')}{d(t - t')}dt'\right] = \frac{5\bar{p}l^4}{384 I}J(t),$$

a result which we might have obtained more easily by applying the correspondence principle for step loading, and for $t > t_1$:

$$w(\tfrac{1}{2}l, t) = \frac{5\bar{p}l^4}{384 I}\int_0^{t_1}\frac{dJ(t - t')}{d(t - t')}dt' = \frac{5\bar{p}l^4}{384 I}(J(t) - J(t - t_1)).$$

A plot of the deflection for a Kelvin beam is shown in Figure 4.5b. If, compared with λ^{-1}, the load is only for a short time on the beam, not much happens; but if t_1 is substantially larger than λ^{-1}, the loading and unloading are clearly separated phenomena.

Figure 4.5c shows the corresponding behavior of a Maxwell beam. As long as the load is present the deflection increases at an even rate; and when the load is removed the beam stays as it is.

Since in all these examples the load was prescribed, the bending moments and the stresses are exactly the same as in an elastic beam, while the deformation is controlled by a hereditary integral. The opposite is true when we prescribe the deflection at one or several points of the structure. Consider the case shown in Figure 4.6a. A beam is supported at three points and carries some load, in which we are not interested since we can evaluate its effect separately and superpose it to the solution that we are about to study here. Under the influence of this load and the ensuing reaction at B, this support sinks slowly and steadily until it has reached a certain displacement w_0, that is, we have

for $0 < t < w_0/c$: $w_B = ct,$ (4.2a)

for $t > w_0/c$: $w_B = w_0.$ (4.2b)

This function may be represented by a diagram, Figure 4.6b, and may be resolved into a sequence of step functions

$$dw'_B = c\, \Delta(t - t')\, dt' \qquad 0 < t' < w_0/c,$$

as we have done before. We may then expect that the beam deflects exactly as an elastic beam would do under the same circumstances, and that all stresses, bending moments, shear forces, and reactions are controlled by

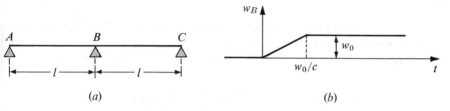

(a)   (b)

FIGURE 4.6. *Continuous beam—a: the beam; b: prescribed displacement of support B.*

hereditary integrals of the type (3.7). In particular, the deflection dw'_B would, in an elastic beam, produce at B the reaction

$$dR'_B = \frac{6EI}{l^3}\, dw'_B$$

and in a viscoelastic beam

$$dR'_B = \frac{6I}{l^3}\, Y(t - t')\, \frac{dw'_B}{dt'}\, dt'.$$

Introduction of dw'_B from (4.2) and integration yields

$$R_B = \frac{6Ic}{l^3} \int_0^{w_0/c} Y(t - t')\, dt'. \tag{4.3}$$

For $t < w_0/c$, one might argue that the upper limit of the integral should rather be t; however, for values of $t' > t$, the relaxation modulus has negative argument and hence equals zero.

To illustrate this formula, we evaluate it for the two simplest materials, using the formulas for $Y(t)$ given in Table 2.2.

For the Maxwell material we find for $t < w_0/c$:

$$R_B = \frac{6Ic}{l^3}\frac{q_1}{p_1} \int_0^t e^{-(t-t')/p_1}\, dt' = \frac{6Icq_1}{l^3}(1 - e^{-t/p_1}),$$

and for $t > w_0/c$:

$$R_B = \frac{6Icq_1}{l^3}(e^{w_0/cp_1} - 1)e^{-t/p_1}.$$

This is represented in Figure 4.7 for two values of the speed c with which the deflection is produced. The maximum of R_B, and hence of all bending moments and of all stresses, occurs when the maximum deflection has just been reached; thereafter the beam relaxes and will ultimately be without stress. Each of the last pair of formulas is applicable at $t = w_0/c$ and yields

$$R_{B\max} = \frac{6Icq_1}{l^3}(1 - e^{-w_0/cp_1}).$$

This maximum depends on c and increases as c is increased. When the total deflection w_B is produced instantaneously, that is, for $c \to \infty$, the right-hand side is an indefinite expression. Expanding the exponential, we find

$$R_{B\max} = \frac{6Iq_1}{l^3}c\left[1 - 1 + \frac{w_0}{cp_1} - \frac{1}{2}\left(\frac{w_0}{cp_1}\right)^2 + -\cdots\right]$$

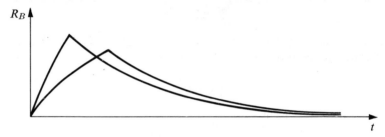

FIGURE 4.7. *Reaction at B for the beam in Figure 4.6.*

and in the limit

$$R_{B\max} = \frac{6Iq_1}{l^3p_1}w_0.$$

The example shows how, in a Maxwell beam, the same deflection needs less force the slower it is applied.

For a Kelvin beam a similar integration yields for $t < w_0/c$:

$$R_B = \frac{6Ic}{l^3}\int_0^{t^+}(q_0 + q_1\,\delta(t - t'))\,dt' = \frac{6Ic}{l^3}(q_0t + q_1),$$

for $t > w_0/c$:

$$R_B = \frac{6Ic}{l^3}\int_0^{w_0/c}q_0\,dt' = \frac{6Iq_0}{l^3}w_0.$$

It is left to the reader to plot and discuss this result.

4.3. Structures Made of Two Materials

In the foregoing examples we used different forms of the correspondence principle, that is, we replaced the actual structure by one of the same dimensions, but made of an elastic material, and then we replaced in all formulas the modulus E by $1/J(t)$ or $Y(t)$ or by an integral operator. This procedure is no longer possible when more than one material is involved. We shall now see what can be done in such cases.

Figure 4.8a shows a continuous beam resting on two rigid supports A and C and on a deformable support B. We assume that the beam is made of some

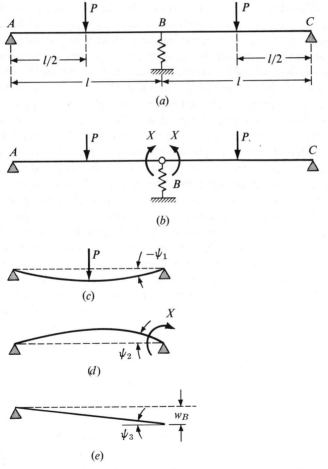

(a)

(b)

(c)

(d)

(e)

FIGURE 4.8. *Viscoelastic beam on elastic support—a: actual system; b: primary system; c–e: deformation of the primary system.*

viscoelastic material described by the differential equation (2.23) or by the creep compliance $J(t)$ or the relaxation modulus $Y(t)$, and that the spring is elastic and has the spring constant k.

The beam may carry any load. To keep the equations simple, the symmetric load arrangement shown in the figure is chosen and the loads are assumed to be applied suddenly at $t = 0$.

This beam is statically indeterminate, that is, the reactions at A, B, and C, and hence the bending moments in the beam, cannot be calculated from the equilibrium conditions alone, but depend on the deformation of the structure. There are several methods of dealing with statically indeterminate structures. We choose the one based on a primary system as shown in Figure 4.8b. This system differs from the actual structure by the presence of a frictionless hinge at B. This has two important consequences: (i) While in the actual continuous beam there is a certain bending moment M_B in the cross section at B, the primary structure, because of the hinge, has at this point a zero moment—unless we apply external couples X as shown to the ends of the beams AB and BC. If we do so, we have $M_B = -X$. (ii) In the actual structure, the tangent to the deflection line has at every point a unique direction. This is not true at the point B of the primary structure, where the ends of the two adjacent spans can and usually do have different slopes. Evidently, the stresses and the deformation of the primary structure (b) and of the actual system (a) will be the same if the magnitude of X is such that there is no discontinuity in the slope of the deflection line at B.

Since the primary structure consists of two simple beams AB and BC, we can easily calculate its deformation. It consists of three parts: (i) the bending of the beams caused by the load P, (ii) the bending of the beams caused by the external couples X, and (iii) the compression of the spring support. The first two of these are deformations of the viscoelastic part of the structure, and hence they are subject to the correspondence principle.

We calculate the slope of the right end of the left beam and call it positive when it represents a clockwise rotation of the tangent from the undeformed into the deformed position. Figures 4.8c–e show the three contributions.

Let I be the moment of inertia of the beam's cross section; then, for an elastic beam of modulus E,

$$\psi_1 = -\frac{Pl^2}{16EI}, \qquad \psi_2 = \frac{Xl}{3EI},$$

formulas which may be found in many books on elementary mechanics of materials. Since P is supposed to be a step function in time, ψ_1 for the viscoelastic beam is

$$\psi_1 = -\frac{Pl^2}{16I} J(t).$$

The moment X is an unknown function of time with, of course, $X(t) \equiv 0$ for $t < 0$. Therefore, ψ_2 must be calculated from the hereditary integral (4.1). We choose (4.1b), write $\psi_2(t)$ for $w(x, t)$, $l/3I$ for $\mathfrak{w}$, and X for f, and have

$$\psi_2 = \frac{l}{3I}\left[X(t)J(0^+) + \int_{0^+}^t X(t') \frac{dJ(t - t')}{d(t - t')}\, dt' \right].$$

Both the loads P and the external couples X lead to a reaction at B. It is

$$R_B = P + \frac{2X(t)}{l}$$

and causes a compression of the spring, that is, a downward displacement of the point B by the amount R_B/k and hence a rigid-body rotation of the entire beam AB in the amount of

$$\psi_3 = \frac{R_B}{kl} = \frac{P}{kl} + \frac{2X(t)}{kl^2}.$$

The total, time dependent, rotation of the right end of the beam AB is $\psi = \psi_1 + \psi_2 + \psi_3$. Because of the symmetry, the left end of BC rotates by the same amount in the opposite sense so that there is a *relative* rotation 2ψ of one end with respect to the other. In the actual beam, Figure 4.8a, there is no such relative rotation because there is no hinge to allow it, and therefore we must choose $X(t)$ such that it makes at all times $\psi \equiv 0$. This is the equation from which X can be calculated. Written out in detail, it reads

$$-\frac{Pl^2}{16I} J(t) + \frac{l}{3I} X(t)J(0^+) + \frac{l}{3I} \int_{0^+}^t X(t') \frac{dJ(t - t')}{d(t - t')}\, dt' + \frac{P}{kl} + \frac{2}{kl^2} X(t) = 0.$$

This equation is similar to (3.8), that is, it is also a Volterra integral equation of the second kind. In the standard form it reads

$$\left(J(0^+) + \frac{6I}{kl^3} \right)X(t) + \int_{0^+}^t X(t') \frac{dJ(t - t')}{d(t - t')}\, dt' = \frac{3Pl}{16}\left(J(t) - \frac{16I}{kl^3} \right). \tag{4.4}$$

4.4. Solution of the Integral Equation

There are several ways to find the solution of (4.4). A straightforward one is to subject it to the Laplace transformation. To do this, we need the *convolution theorem*, which we shall now derive.

The integral in (4.4) has the form

$$h(t) = \int_0^t f(t')g(t - t')\, dt. \tag{4.5}$$

Its Laplace transform is

$$\bar{h}(s) = \int_0^\infty e^{-st} \int_0^t f(t')g(t-t')\,dt'\,dt.$$

The integration interval is the shaded area in Figure 4.9. When we interchange the order of integrations, we have

$$\bar{h}(s) = \int_0^\infty \int_{t'}^\infty e^{-st} f(t')g(t-t')\,dt\,dt'$$

$$= \int_0^\infty \int_{t'}^\infty e^{-s(t-t')}e^{-st'}f(t')g(t-t')\,dt\,dt'.$$

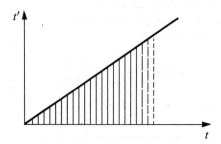

FIGURE 4.9. *Integration domain.*

Since in the inner integral t' is held constant, we can replace dt by $d(t-t')$ and, with $t-t' = \tau$, we can write

$$\bar{h}(s) = \int_0^\infty e^{-st'}f(t')\,dt' \int_0^\infty e^{-s\tau}\bar{g}(\tau)\,d\tau = \bar{f}(s)\bar{g}(s).$$

The integral (4.5) is called the convolution of $f(t)$ and $g(t)$, and the convolution theorem states that the Laplace transform of the convolution is the product of the two transforms $\bar{f}$ and $\bar{g}$.

With the help of this theorem the Laplace transform of (4.4) may now be written:

$$\left[J(0^+) + \frac{6I}{kl^3}\right]\bar{X}(s) + \bar{X}(s)[s\bar{J}(s) - J(0^+)] = \frac{3Pl}{16}\left[\bar{J}(s) - \frac{16I}{kl^3 s}\right]. \quad (4.6)$$

This is an algebraic equation for $\bar{X}(s)$. After solving it, the inverse Laplace transformation is applied to obtain $X(t)$.

For a Maxwell material, we have

$$J(t) = \frac{p_1 + t}{q_1}, \qquad \bar{J}(s) = \frac{p_1 s + 1}{q_1 s^2},$$

and (4.6) assumes the following form:

$$\left[\frac{p_1}{q_1} + \frac{6I}{kl^3} + \frac{1}{q_1 s}\right] \bar{X}(s) = \frac{3Pl}{16}\left[\frac{p_1 s + 1}{q_1 s^2} - \frac{16I}{kl^3 s}\right].$$

We solve for $\bar{X}(s)$ and collect terms to obtain

$$\bar{X}(s) = \frac{3Pl}{16} \frac{(p_1 kl^3 - 16Iq_1)s + kl^3}{s[(p_1 kl^3 + 6Iq_1)s + kl^3]}.$$

To transform this back to the variable t, we use pairs (3) and (4) of Table 2.1 and, after a few lines of algebra, arrive at the following result:

$$X(t) = \frac{3Pl}{16}\left[1 - \frac{22Iq_1}{p_1 kl^3 + 6Iq_1}\exp\left(-\frac{kl^3 t}{p_1 kl^3 + 6Iq_1}\right)\right]. \qquad (4.7)$$

To understand this formula, we compare the viscoelastic beam with an elastic one. In an elastic beam, the moment X is, of course, independent of time, and we could easily find its value by repeating the analysis, using for ψ_1 and ψ_2 the elastic formulas given on p. 42. The use of the Laplace transformation is then, of course, not necessary. However, we may use a limiting process to extract the elastic solution from (4.7).

The Maxwell model degenerates into a simple spring if the dashpot is immobilized. Correspondingly, the differential equation of the Maxwell fluid assumes the form $\dot{\sigma} = E\dot{\varepsilon}$ if we let $p_1 \to \infty$ while keeping $q_1/p_1 = E$ constant. When we perform this process in (4.7), the argument of the exponential function goes to zero and we obtain

$$X = \frac{3Pl}{16}\left[1 - \frac{22EI}{kl^3 + 6EI}\right] = \frac{3Pl}{16}\frac{kl^3 - 16EI}{kl^3 + 6EI}. \qquad (4.8)$$

Returning to the Maxwell beam, we see that $X(0)$ equals the value from (4.8) if we use for E the impact modulus $E_0 = q_1/p_1$ of the Maxwell material. As time goes by, the moment X increases and tends to the limit

$$X(\infty) = 3Pl/16.$$

As may readily be seen from (4.8), this is the moment to occur in an elastic beam for $k \to \infty$, that is, for a *rigid* support at B.

The physical background of these results is easy to understand. We saw on p. 7 that at the instant of loading the Maxwell fluid behaves like an elastic solid of modulus E_0, and that if the load persists, the deformation is unbounded. Therefore the beam behaves initially like an elastic beam, but ultimately the deformation of the elastic spring (which necessarily is bounded) becomes negligible compared to the ever increasing deflection of the beam.

It should be kept in mind that all our formulas are based on the assumption of small deflections and hence become invalid when the deflection of the beam keeps growing.

The reader who is not familiar enough with the Laplace transformation may solve the integral equation (4.4) in the following way: Since we have seen that many viscoelastic processes are exponential in time, it is plausible that X might have the form

$$X(t) = C_1 + C_2 e^{-\lambda t}.$$

When one introduces this together with $J(t)$ for the Maxwell fluid in (4.4), the integral may be evaluated and one finds an equation containing terms linear in t, terms with $e^{-\lambda t}$, and constants. Each of these must separately add up to zero, and this yields three equations, from which one calculates C_1, C_2, and λ. The result is in agreement with (4.7).

4.5. Differential Equation of the Beam

We solved the last problem by applying the correspondence principle to the viscoelastic part of the structure. If the solution for the corresponding elastic problem is readily available, this is the proper thing to do. Otherwise, however, it seems to be a detour to find first the solution to a problem in which we are not interested and then to derive from it the one for the problem at hand. To avoid this detour, we need the differential equation of the viscoelastic beam.

In any beam, we have the well-known equilibrium relations:

$$V' = -p, \qquad M' = V, \qquad M'' = -p, \qquad \text{(4.9a–c)}$$

where, as usual, M and V are bending moment and shear force as shown in Figure 4.10a, p is the load per unit length of the beam, and the primes stand for derivatives with respect to x. Since in a viscoelastic beam all quantities depend also on time, the primes should be understood as indicating partial differentiation.

Besides (4.9a–c) we have for the elastic beam the elastic relation

$$w'' = -M/EI. \qquad \text{(4.10)}$$

We now derive its equivalent under the assumption that the beam material obeys the viscoelastic law (2.23).

Figure 4.10b shows in heavy lines a beam element before deformation, and in thin lines its deformed shape. The cross sections at its ends were originally both vertical, but on the deformed element they make an angle

$d\psi = \kappa\, dx$, where κ is the curvature of the beam axis. If the deflection w of the beam is small enough to make $(w')^2 \ll 1$, then

$$\kappa = -w'',$$

as is known from elastic beams.

We choose in the cross section, Figure 4.10c, an arbitrary area element $dA = dy \cdot dz$ and consider the corresponding "fiber" of length dx in the beam element. In the deformed state it is stretched by the amount $z\, d\psi$, whence its strain

$$\epsilon = \frac{z\, d\psi}{dx} = z\kappa.$$

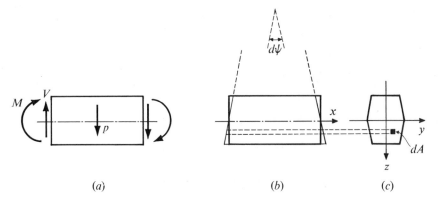

(a)   *(b)*   *(c)*

FIGURE 4.10. *Beam element.*

Across the area element dA a stress σ is acting, which is related to ϵ by (2.23). The force $\sigma\, dA$ makes a contribution to the bending moment M transmitted in the cross section,

$$M = \int_A \sigma z\, dA.$$

To this equation we apply the operator $\mathbf{P}$ of (2.23c) and then replace $\mathbf{P}(\sigma)$ by $\mathbf{Q}(\epsilon)$ to obtain

$$\mathbf{P}(M) = \int_A \mathbf{P}(\sigma)z\, dA = \int_A \mathbf{Q}(\epsilon)z\, dA = \int_A \mathbf{Q}(\kappa z)z\, dA.$$

$\mathbf{Q}$ is a linear operator containing only time derivatives. Therefore, we may pull z out from under it and then $\mathbf{Q}(\kappa)$ out of the integral, which yields

$$\mathbf{P}(M) = \int_A \mathbf{Q}(\kappa)z^2\, dA = \mathbf{Q}(\kappa)\int_A z^2\, dA = \mathbf{Q}(\kappa) \cdot I,$$

where I is the moment of inertia of the cross section with respect to the y axis which must pass through the centroid for the same reason as in an elastic

beam. When we still express the curvature in terms of the deflection, we
arrive finally at the differential equation

$$I\mathbf{Q}(w'') = -\mathbf{P}(M).\tag{4.11}$$

It may be combined with (4.9c) to yield

$$I\mathbf{Q}(w^{iv}) = \mathbf{P}(p),\tag{4.12}$$

which corresponds to the well-known equation

$$EI\,w^{iv} = p$$

of the elastic beam. In x it is of the fourth order, but its order in time derivatives depends on the special choice of the operators $\mathbf{P}$ and $\mathbf{Q}$.

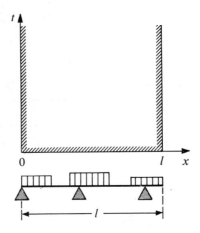

FIGURE 4.11. *Semi-infinite strip in the x, t-plane.*

Once the deflection $w(x, t)$ of a beam is known, M and V may be found
from (4.11) and (4.9b), respectively. Solving the problem for a viscoelastic beam of length l (no matter how supported) means finding the solution
of (4.12) for a semi-infinite strip in the x, t-plane which is bounded by the
x axis and the lines $x = 0$ and $x = l$, Figure 4.11. Just as in the elastic case,
we need to know two boundary conditions at each end of the beam, prescribing there w or V and w' or M. In addition, we need initial conditions
for $t = 0$ and $0 \leq x \leq l$, their number depending on the operator $\mathbf{Q}$ (which
is never lower than the order of $\mathbf{P}$, see Tables 2.2 and 2.3, pp. 16 and 19).

4.6. General Correspondence Principle

We use an example to explain the general form of the correspondence
principle, considering again the beam of Figure 4.8, but replacing the con-
centrated forces by a distributed load $p(x, t)$, of which we require only that it

be symmetric with respect to the point B in Figure 4.12. This symmetry allows us to restrict our attention to the left span AB.

The deflection $w(x, t)$ in this span is governed by the partial differential equation (4.12). There are four boundary conditions. At the left end the deflection and the bending moment are zero for all times t:

$$x = 0: \quad w = 0, \quad M = 0.$$

At the right end, symmetry requires a zero slope, and the shear force must be equal to half the reaction $R_B = kw$. With due consideration of the sign convention of the shear force, this yields

$$x = l: \quad w' = 0, \quad V = M' = -\tfrac{1}{2}kw.$$

As initial conditions we assume that w and as many of its time derivatives as needed are zero at $t = 0$ and for $0 \leq x \leq l$.

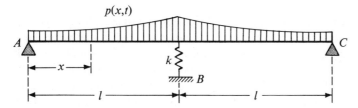

$p(x,t)$

FIGURE 4.12. *Viscoelastic beam on elastic support.*

We now subject the differential equation and the boundary conditions to the Laplace transformation. On the right-hand side of (4.12) we have

$$\mathbf{P}(p) = \left(p_0 + p_1 \frac{\partial}{\partial} + p_2 \frac{\partial^2}{\partial t^2} + \cdots \right) p.$$

When we apply the Laplace transformation to each of these terms, we obtain

$$(p_0 + p_1 s + p_2 s^2 + p_3 s^3 + \cdots) \bar{p} = \mathscr{P}(s) \cdot \bar{p},$$

and similarly the left hand side yields $I \mathscr{Q}(s) \cdot \bar{w}^{iv}$, where $\mathscr{P}(s)$ and $\mathscr{Q}(s)$ are the polynomials defined by (2.26).

With this notation the Laplace transforms of our equations may be written as follows:

$$I \mathscr{Q}(s)\bar{w}^{iv}(x, s) = \mathscr{P}(s)\bar{p}(x, s), \tag{4.13a}$$

$$x = 0: \quad \bar{w} = 0, \tag{4.13b}$$

$$\mathscr{P}(s)\bar{M} = -I \mathscr{Q}(s)\bar{w}'' = 0, \quad \therefore \ \bar{w}'' = 0 \tag{4.13c}$$

$$x = l: \quad \bar{w}' = 0, \tag{4.13d}$$

$$-\tfrac{1}{2}k\mathscr{P}(s)\bar{w} = \mathscr{P}(s)\bar{M}' = -I \mathscr{Q}(s)\bar{w}''',$$

$$\therefore \ \bar{w}''' - \frac{k}{2I} \frac{\mathscr{P}(s)}{\mathscr{Q}(s)} \bar{w} = 0. \tag{4.13e}$$

For comparison we now list the equations which would apply to an elastic beam of modulus E and a time-dependent load $p(x, t)$:

$$EIw^{iv}(x, t) = p(x, t), \tag{4.14a}$$

$$x = 0: \quad w = 0, \qquad w'' = 0, \tag{4.14b,c}$$

$$x = l: \quad w' = 0, \tag{4.14d}$$

$$-\tfrac{1}{2}kw = V = M' = -EIw''',$$

$$\therefore \ w''' - \frac{k}{2EI}w = 0. \tag{4.14e}$$

These two sets of equations are identical if we let

$$\widehat{E} = \mathcal{Q}(s)/\mathcal{P}(s) \tag{4.15}$$

and equate $p(x, t)$, $w(x, t)$ of the elastic beam with $\bar{p}(x, s)$, $\bar{w}(x, s)$ of the visco-elastic one. Obviously, this result is not restricted to the particular case for which we have just found it. For any beam, frame, or arch we would have boundary conditions in terms of w and its first three derivatives with respect to x, and since the Laplace transform of (2.23c) and Hooke's law are related by (4.15), the Laplace transform of any boundary condition would show the same arrangement of the polynomials $\mathcal{P}(s)$ and $\mathcal{Q}(s)$ which would relate it via (4.15) to its elastic counterpart.

Thus we have arrived at the most general form of the *correspondence principle*, which we can formulate for beam structures:

To find the stresses in and the deformation of a viscoelastic beam structure, solve the corresponding elastic problem, replace E by $\mathcal{Q}(s)/\mathcal{P}(s)$, and the ensuing functions are the Laplace transforms of the solution of the visco-elastic problem.

Example

As an example, we use the beam of Figure 4.12, assuming a uniformly distributed load applied at $t = 0$ and then held constant:

$$p(x, t) = p\Delta(t).$$

The solution of the corresponding elastic problem for the left span is

$$w(x) = \frac{p}{24EI}\left[(8l^3 - 4lx^2 + x^3)x - \frac{5kl^4}{2(6EI + kl^3)}(3l^2 - x^2)x\right]$$

and it will be assumed that the reader either knows how to obtain it or that he is willing to accept it on good faith.

Now let the beam be made of a Maxwell material with

$$\boxed{\mathscr{P}(s) = 1 + p_1 s, \qquad \mathscr{Q}(s) = q_1 s}$$

according to the third column of Table 2.2. The Laplace transform of the step function load is $\bar{p} = p/s$, and the correspondence principle yields for $\bar{w}(x, s)$ the formula

$$\bar{w} = \frac{p}{24Iq_1} \frac{1 + p_1 s}{s^2} \left[(8l^3 - 4lx^2 + x^3)x \right.$$

$$\left. - \frac{5kl^4(1 + p_1 s)}{2[6Iq_1 s + kl^3(1 + p_1 s)]} (3l^2 - x^2)x \right].$$

To transform this back into $w(x, t)$, we need the pairs (3), (4), (5) of Table 2.1. The calculation involves some lengthy algebra, but it does not present any other difficulties. It yields the following result:

$$w(x, t) = \frac{5p}{8kl^2} \left[1 - \frac{6Iq_1}{6Iq_1 + kl^3 p_1} e^{-\lambda t} \right] (3l^2 - x^2)x$$

$$+ \frac{p}{48Iq_1} (p_1 + t)(l^3 - 3lx^2 + 2x^3)x$$

with

$$\lambda = \frac{kl^3}{6Iq_1 + kl^3 p_1}$$

Its physical interpretation may follow the same lines as that given on p. 45.

Exercises

4.1. A cantilever beam of span l is made of a three-parameter solid. It carries at its tip a load P, which depends on time according to one or the other of the load histories shown in Figure 4.13 (the last of these is a sine curve). Find the deflection of the tip of the beam. For an elastic beam, the deflection is

$$w(l) = \frac{Pl^3}{3EI} .$$

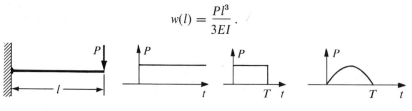

FIGURE 4.13.

4.2. A viscoelastic beam of span l carries a chain of three beamlets connected by hinges. Over these a load P is moving at constant speed c from left to

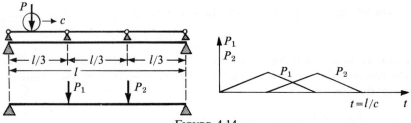

FIGURE 4.14.

right. For the main beam, this produces loads P_1 and P_2, which vary as shown in Figure 4.14. Find the bending moment and the deflection for the midspan point. Start from the solution of the elastic problem, which can be found in many books.

4.3. The beam shown in Figure 4.15 has pin supports, but the rotation θ of its ends is restrained by viscoelastic springs. Let the beam be made of a Kelvin material described by (2.9), and let the reactive moment M of each spring be related to the end rotation of the beam by a Maxwell law:

$$M + m_1\dot{M} = n_1\dot{\theta}.$$

Establish an integral equation for the common value M of the moments at both ends of the beam. Solve it and plot as functions of time the bending moments at $x = 0$ and $x = l/2$ and the deflection at the midspan point.

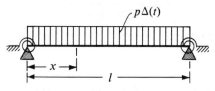

FIGURE 4.15.

4.4. Reconsider the beam shown in Figure 4.8, but assume that only in the left span a load P is acting. Establish the integral equation for the redundant moment X and solve it for the case that the spring obeys the Kelvin law.

4.5. A beam has a rectangular cross section built up of two different viscoelastic materials, as shown in Figure 4.16. The relaxation moduli of these

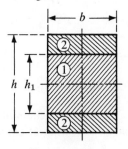

FIGURE 4.16.

materials are Y_1 and Y_2. Find the relaxation modulus of the beam, that is, a function $Y(t)$ such that the bending moment $M = Y(t)$ if the curvature is $\kappa = \Delta(t)$.

4.6. Assume that in the beam cross section of Figure 4.16 the core material is elastic (modulus E) and that material 2 is a three-parameter solid. Derive a relation of type (4.11) between bending moment and curvature.

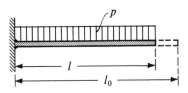

FIGURE 4.17.

4.7. A cantilever beam of span l_0 is made of a Maxwell material (Figure 4.17). At $t = 0$ it receives its load p and at the same time begins to burn or to melt from its tip so that at time t its length is $l = l_0 - ct$. Find the deflection as a function of x and t.

There are two ways to solve this problem: (i) establishing the proper boundary conditions and then solving (4.12), or (ii) calculating the statically determinate bending moments, then w'' from (4.11) and by integration for constant time the deflection w.

It is suggested that the first approach be used for solving the problem, and the second for checking the solution.

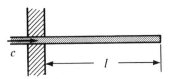

FIGURE 4.18.

4.8. A bar of constant cross section is extruded horizontally from an orifice (Figure 4.18). At time t its length is $l = ct$. The bar carries its own weight as a cantilever. Find the deflection.

REFERENCE

For information on related problems in the theory of elasticity see

[18] S. TIMOSHENKO and J. N. GOODIER, *Theory of Elasticity* (2nd ed.) (New York: McGraw-Hill, 1951), pp. 258–280 (torsion of prismatic bars), and pp. 304–313 (torsion of shafts of variable diameter).

CHAPTER 5

Vibrations

ALL VISCOELASTIC DEFORMATIONS vary with time, that is, there is always some motion taking place. Whenever the velocity changes, there must be an unbalance of forces producing the acceleration. However, most viscoelastic motion is so slow that the product of acceleration and mass is very small compared to other forces present. It is this fact that made it possible to develop a substantial part of the theory without introducing inertia terms into the equations. It is clear that mass inertia becomes an important feature as soon as we wish to deal with vibrations, and this field we now shall enter.

5.1. Complex Compliance

Before actually introducing inertia terms and writing dynamic equations, we must examine the constitutive equation of the viscoelastic material for the special case that stress and strain are oscillating functions of time. This means essentially an interpretation of (2.23) or any of its equivalents, and this task may be approached in two different ways. Either we apply an oscillating stress $\sigma = \sigma_0 \sin \omega t$ to a tension specimen and ask for the strain it produces, or we force upon the specimen a deformation described by an oscillating strain and ask for the stress that will be produced. While the first approach may seem more natural, the second one has the advantage of not leading to minus signs at inconvenient places.

Instead of assuming ϵ to vary like a sine or cosine of time, it will be advantageous to write

$$\epsilon = \epsilon_0 e^{i\omega t} = \epsilon_0(\cos \omega t + i \sin \omega t). \tag{5.1}$$

In this formula the real and imaginary parts represent, each by itself, two oscillatory strains of the frequency ω. Since (2.23b) has real coefficients p_k

and q_k, the real part of the solution σ will correspond to the real part of ϵ and similarly, the imaginary parts of σ and ϵ correspond to each other. In this way we get simultaneously the solutions to two closely related problems, at the same time having the additional advantage of greater simplicity of the mathematical formalism.

When we introduce ϵ from (5.1) into (2.23b), we see that also the stress must have a factor $e^{i\omega t}$, that is,

$$\sigma = \sigma_0 e^{i\omega t}. \tag{5.2}$$

Equation (2.23b) then reads

$$\sum_0^m p_k \sigma_0 (i\omega)^k e^{i\omega t} = \sum_0^n q_k \epsilon_0 (i\omega)^k e^{i\omega t},$$

and after cancellation of $e^{i\omega t}$ this may be solved for the stress amplitude

$$\sigma_0 = \epsilon_0 \frac{\sum q_k i^k \omega^k}{\sum p_k i^k \omega^k} = \frac{\mathcal{Q}(i\omega)}{\mathcal{P}(i\omega)}, \tag{5.3}$$

where $\mathcal{P}$ and $\mathcal{Q}$ are the polynomials introduced in (2.26). Evidently, σ_0 is a complex quantity and may be written as

$$\sigma_0 = \sigma_1 + i\sigma_2, \tag{5.4}$$

whence

$$\sigma = \sigma_0 e^{i\omega t} = (\sigma_1 + i\sigma_2)(\cos \omega t + i \sin \omega t)$$

and, after separation of real and imaginary parts,

$$\sigma = (\sigma_1 \cos \omega t - \sigma_2 \sin \omega t) + i(\sigma_2 \cos \omega t + \sigma_1 \sin \omega t). \tag{5.5}$$

The real part of σ is the stress response to $\epsilon = \epsilon_0 \cos \omega t$, and the imaginary part is the response to a strain $\epsilon = \epsilon_0 \sin \omega t$. In both cases the stress is a mixture of a sine and a cosine oscillation, that is, there is a phase shift between stress and strain, and they reach their peak values at different times.

The relation between σ and ϵ may be visualized in a vector diagram similar to those used in other fields of vibration theory. This diagram (Figure 5.1) has two pairs of orthogonal axes, R, I and r, i. The axes R, I are a coordinate system, in which we plot points with the coordinates σ_1, σ_2 and ϵ_0, 0 and vectors $\boldsymbol{\sigma}$ and $\boldsymbol{\epsilon}$ which have these coordinates as their components. We call these vectors the amplitude vectors of the oscillating quantities σ and ϵ.

The axes r, i revolve clockwise with the angular velocity ω. When we now project at any time t the vectors $\boldsymbol{\sigma}$ and $\boldsymbol{\epsilon}$ on the axis r, we find the component vectors

$$\sigma_1 \cos \omega t - \sigma_2 \sin \omega t \quad \text{and} \quad \epsilon_0 \cos \omega t,$$

that is, the real parts of the right-hand sides of (5.5) and (5.1). Similarly, the projections of $\boldsymbol{\sigma}$ and $\boldsymbol{\epsilon}$ on the axis i are the imaginary parts of the oscillating quantities σ and ϵ. The angle ψ between the two amplitude vectors describes the phase shift of the oscillations. The r axis (and also the i axis) coincides first with $\boldsymbol{\sigma}$ and by a time $t = \psi/\omega$ later with $\boldsymbol{\epsilon}$. This means that σ reaches its peak value that much earlier than ϵ.

So far, we have assumed that ϵ_0 is real, that is, that $\boldsymbol{\epsilon}$ coincides with the R axis of Figure 5.1. It would not make much of a difference if we would rotate the vectors $\boldsymbol{\epsilon}$ and $\boldsymbol{\sigma}$ by any angle, as long as we preserve the phase angle ψ between them. Stress and strain would then reach their maxima or pass through zero by a certain time earlier or later without any change in

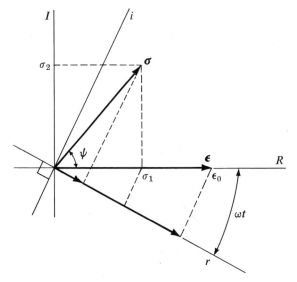

FIGURE 5.1. *Representation of a vibration by complex vectors.*

their relations to each other, that is, the whole oscillation would be shifted in phase. If we make use of this possibility of generalizing our formulas, ϵ_0 will become complex—let us say, $\epsilon_0 = \epsilon_1 + i\epsilon_2$—but (5.3) will not be affected.

Since the differential equation (2.23) is linear, it is not surprising that (5.3) is a linear relation between σ_0 and ϵ_0. We write it in the form

$$\epsilon_0 = G(\omega) \cdot \sigma_0 \tag{5.6}$$

and call the factor

$$G(\omega) = \frac{\mathscr{P}(i\omega)}{\mathscr{Q}(i\omega)} = G_1(\omega) + iG_2(\omega) \tag{5.7}$$

the *complex compliance*. It depends on the frequency, but not on the amplitude of stress or strain or on time. Assuming the general case that both ϵ_0 and σ_0 are complex, we may write (5.6) in the form

$$(\epsilon_1 + i\epsilon_2) = (G_1 + iG_2)(\sigma_1 + i\sigma_2),$$

from which we see that

$$\epsilon_1 = G_1\sigma_1 - G_2\sigma_2, \qquad \epsilon_2 = G_2\sigma_1 + G_1\sigma_2. \tag{5.8}$$

Solving these equations for σ_1, σ_2, we find

$$(G_1^2 + G_2^2)\sigma_1 = G_1\epsilon_1 + G_2\epsilon_2, \tag{5.9a}$$

$$(G_1^2 + G_2^2)\sigma_2 = G_1\epsilon_2 - G_2\epsilon_1, \tag{5.9b}$$

and these two pairs of equations show us what strain is produced by a given stress and what stress by a given strain. In view of later needs we let $\sigma_1 = 1$, $\sigma_2 = 0$ and see from (5.8) that then $\epsilon_1 = G_1$, $\epsilon_2 = G_2$. From the real parts of (5.1) and (5.2) it then follows that a unit oscillatory stress $\sigma = \cos \omega t$ produces the strain

$$\epsilon = G_1(\omega) \cos \omega t - G_2(\omega) \sin \omega t, \tag{5.10a}$$

and from the imaginary parts that $\sigma = \sin \omega t$ produces

$$\epsilon = G_2(\omega) \cos \omega t + G_1(\omega) \sin \omega t. \tag{5.10b}$$

5.2. Dissipation

We consider an element of a tension bar of cross section A and length dx. At its ends forces σA are acting, and in the time dt the strain increases by $\dot{\epsilon} \, dt$. This makes the forces do the work

$$\sigma A \cdot dx \, \dot{\epsilon} \, dt = dW A \, dx,$$

where dW is the work done per unit volume of the bar. If the deformation continues for a finite time, the work done on a unit volume is

$$W = \int dW = \int \sigma\dot{\epsilon} \, dt. \tag{5.11}$$

This work comes from an outside source of energy and goes into the element. In an elastic bar it creates potential energy (strain energy), which will be recovered upon unloading. In a viscoelastic material part or even all of this energy may be lost in the sense that it is transformed into heat and therefore is not recoverable. We call such energy *dissipated*.

In (5.11), the stress may be any function of time, increasing or decreasing, or a constant. We shall now apply this formula to the special case of an oscillating stress, accompanied by an oscillating strain. However, in doing so, we cannot use the complex notation of (5.1) and (5.2). This notation represents, as we have seen, the simultaneous handling of two oscillations having a phase difference of 90°, keeping them apart by multiplying one of them by a factor i. Now, our work integral contains the product of stress and strain, and in this product the imaginary stress working on an imaginary strain would do a negative, but real, work so that the real part of W would be an unidentifiable mixture of the work done by both oscillations, while the imaginary part would be entirely meaningless. We therefore resort to writing stress and strain in real quantities, choosing

$$\sigma = \sigma_0 \cos \omega t \qquad \text{and} \qquad \epsilon = \sigma_0[G_1(\omega) \cos \omega t - G_2(\omega) \sin \omega t].$$

We then have

$$W = -\sigma_0^2 \omega \int \cos \omega t (G_1 \sin \omega t + G_2 \cos \omega t) \, dt. \qquad (5.12)$$

It is now necessary to choose limits for the integral. Two such choices are of interest: We may integrate over one period $T = 2\pi/\omega$, or we may integrate over a unit of time.

Let us begin with the integral over one period and write

$$W = -\sigma_0^2 \omega G_1 \int_0^T \cos \omega t \sin \omega t \, dt - \sigma_0^2 \omega G_2 \int_0^T \cos^2 \omega t \, dt.$$

The first of the two integrals is zero. It represents the work done by σ on a deformation which is in phase with the stress. This is the kind of work encountered in elastic materials. Through half the period energy is pumped into the material, and in the other half it is recovered. In a viscoelastic material the strain has another component, which is by 90° out of phase with (in quadrature with) the stress and this one makes a permanent contribution:

$$W = -\sigma_0^2 \omega G_2 \frac{\pi}{\omega} = -\pi \sigma_0^2 G_2(\omega). \qquad (5.13)$$

During every period of the oscillation this amount of work is done, and the corresponding energy is dissipated. Since the second law of thermodynamics requires that this dissipated energy be non-negative, we learn from (5.13) that

$$G_2(\omega) \leqq 0, \qquad (5.14)$$

and we shall see that the equal sign applies only in some limiting cases.

In applications it is of more interest to know the energy dissipated in a unit of time. We call this the *dissipation* D and find it by dividing W from (5.13) by $T = 2\pi/\omega$:

$$D = -\tfrac{1}{2}\sigma_0^2 \omega G_2(\omega). \qquad (5.15)$$

If we try to verify this formula from (5.12), we find that it checks only if there is an integer number of periods T in the time unit. Otherwise there is a small deviation, positive or negative, which depends on how the time unit is cut out of the sequence of ups and downs of the oscillation. This indicates that D is an average quantity and does not make sense when we are interested in the energy turnover within a few seconds, while the period T is of the order of minutes or hours.

5.3. Application to Specific Materials

We shall now use the concepts of complex compliance and dissipation to see how some of our standard materials behave under oscillating stress.

We begin with the three-parameter solid. From (5.7) and the differential equation (2.19) we find

$$G(\omega) = \frac{1 + p_1 i\omega}{q_0 + q_1 i\omega}, \tag{5.16}$$

which, after multiplying numerator and denominator by $(q_0 - q_1 i\omega)$, can be separated into real and imaginary parts:

$$G_1(\omega) = \frac{q_0 + p_1 q_1 \omega^2}{q_0^2 + q_1^2 \omega^2}, \qquad G_2(\omega) = -\frac{(q_1 - p_1 q_0)\omega}{q_0^2 + q_1^2 \omega^2}. \tag{5.17}$$

We saw that G_2 must be negative, and this leads us back to the inequality (2.20), which here acquires a new significance.

From (5.10a) we see that, in our material, a stress $\sigma = \cos \omega t$ produces a strain

$$\epsilon = \frac{q_0 + p_1 q_1 \omega^2}{q_0^2 + q_1^2 \omega^2} \cos \omega t + \frac{(q_1 - p_1 q_0)\omega}{q_0^2 + q_1^2 \omega^2} \sin \omega t. \tag{5.18}$$

Since the sine lags in phase 90° behind the cosine, the strain is between 0° and 90° behind the stress. When we let ω approach zero or infinity, the coefficient of $\sin \omega t$ goes to zero, and the phase difference between σ and ϵ tends to disappear, that is, the material approaches elastic behavior. In particular, we have

$$\text{for} \quad \omega \approx 0: \qquad \epsilon \approx \frac{1}{q_0} \cos \omega t = \frac{1}{E_\infty} \cos \omega t,$$

$$\text{for} \quad \omega \to \infty: \qquad \epsilon \to \frac{p_1}{q_1} \cos \omega t = \frac{1}{E_0} \cos \omega t$$

with the moduli E_∞ and E_0 as defined on pp. 7 and 8.

In a coordinate system G_1, G_2, (5.17) is the parameter representation of a curve (Figure 5.2a). It may be left to the reader to show that it is a semicircle.

The dissipation can be calculated from (5.15) and (5.17). It is

$$D = \tfrac{1}{2}\sigma_0^2 \frac{(q_1 - p_1 q_0)\omega^2}{q_0^2 + q_1^2 \omega^2}.\tag{5.19}$$

For $\omega \to \infty$, it approaches a finite value, but for $\omega = 0$ it vanishes. This indicates that in the latter case the material truly approaches elastic behavior, while at high frequency there is little dissipation per cycle, but there are so many cycles per unit of time that their combined contribution does not vanish.

Our results include as limiting cases the Kelvin solid and the Maxwell fluid.

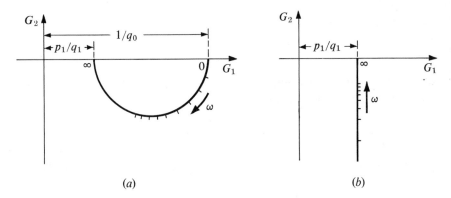

FIGURE 5.2. *Complex compliances—a: three-parameter solid; b: Maxwell fluid.*

As may be seen from the third column of Table 2.2, the three-parameter solid degenerates into the Kelvin solid if we let $p_1 = 0$. This leads to quantitative changes in G_2 and D, but to a qualitative change of G_1, which is now

$$G_1(\omega) = \frac{q_0}{q_0^2 + q_1^2 \omega^2}.$$

For $\omega \to \infty$ this goes to zero as ω^{-2}, while G_2 tends to zero only as ω^{-1}. This means that at high frequencies the phase shift between stress and strain approaches 90° and that the behavior of the Kelvin solid approaches that of a viscous fluid. In Figure 5.2a, the half circle reaches at its left end the origin of the coordinate system.

If in (5.16) through (5.19) we keep p_1 but let $q_0 = 0$, we have the results for the Maxwell fluid. In this case the right end of the half circle in Figure 5.2a moves to infinity and the curve becomes a vertical straight line, as is shown in

Figure 5.2b. Both parts of the complex compliance change substantially and are now

$$G_1(\omega) = \frac{p_1}{q_1}, \qquad G_2(\omega) = -\frac{1}{q_1 \omega}. \tag{5.20}$$

G_2 still vanishes when $\omega \to \infty$, but for $\omega \to 0$ it becomes infinite and outweighs G_1 in importance. This means that for high frequencies the Maxwell material approaches elastic behavior, while for low ones it becomes purely viscous. The dissipation turns out to be independent of the frequency:

$$D = \sigma_0^2 / 2q_1. \tag{5.21}$$

The results contained in (5.17) and (5.20) and similar expressions for other materials are listed in the last two columns of Table 2.2.

5.4. Relations between the Compliances

So far we have derived expressions for the complex compliance $G(\omega)$ from the differential equation (2.23) of the material. The existence of the hereditary integral (3.6) proves that the creep compliance $J(t)$ completely determines the strain produced by a given stress. Therefore, it must be possible to calculate $G(\omega)$ when only $J(t)$ is known. Now, as we have seen in (5.10a), the stress $\sigma = \cos \omega t$ produces the periodic strain $\epsilon = G_1 \cos \omega t - G_2 \sin \omega t$. However, if we start applying such a stress at $t = 0$, the strain may not be a simple oscillation, but may contain a transient part. We try to remove this transient by postulating that the oscillatory stress has already been acting for a very long (an infinite) time, let us say, since $t = -T$. Then, with an obvious modification, the hereditary integral (3.6a) yields the strain

$$\epsilon(t) = \sigma(-T) \cdot J(t + T) + \int_{-T}^{t} J(t - t') \frac{d\sigma(t')}{dt'} dt'$$

and, with $T \to \infty$, we expect this to be the strain described by (5.10a):

$G_1(\omega) \cos \omega t - G_2(\omega) \sin \omega t$

$$= \lim_{T \to \infty} \left\{ J(t + T) \cos \omega T - \omega \int_{-T}^{t} J(t - t') \sin \omega t' \, dt' \right\}. \tag{5.22}$$

We shall study the working of this formula by applying it to two typical materials, a solid and a fluid.

For a Kelvin solid with $J(t)$ from Table 2.2, we have

$G_1 \cos \omega t - G_2 \sin \omega t$

$$= \frac{1}{q_0} \lim_{T \to \infty} \left\{ (1 - e^{-\lambda(t+T)}) \cos \omega T - \omega \int_{-T}^{t} (1 - e^{-\lambda t} e^{\lambda t'}) \sin \omega t' \, dt' \right\}$$

with $\lambda = q_0/q_1$. In the term preceding the integral, the exponential tends to zero and may be dropped immediately. After performing the integration, we then have

$$G_1 \cos \omega t - G_2 \sin \omega t = \frac{1}{q_0} \lim_{T \to \infty} \left\{ \cos \omega T + [\cos \omega t']^t_{-T} \right.$$

$$\left. + \frac{\omega e^{-\lambda t}}{\lambda^2 + \omega^2} [(\lambda \sin \omega t' - \omega \cos \omega t')e^{\lambda t'}]^t_{-T} \right\}.$$

When the integration limits are introduced in the bracketed terms, some cancellations take place, and then the expression is reduced to

$$G_1 \cos \omega t - G_2 \sin \omega t = \frac{1}{q_0} \left\{ \cos \omega t + \frac{\lambda \omega}{\lambda^2 + \omega^2} \sin \omega t - \frac{\omega^2}{\lambda^2 + \omega^2} \cos \omega t \right\}.$$

This really is a harmonic oscillation, and by separating sine and cosine parts one obtains G_1 and G_2 as listed in Table 2.2.

For the Maxwell fluid we start out with

$$G_1 \cos \omega t - G_2 \sin \omega t$$

$$= \frac{1}{q_1} \lim_{T \to \infty} \left\{ (p_1 + t + T) \cos \omega t - \omega \int_{-T}^{t} (p_1 + t - t') \sin \omega t' \, dt' \right\}.$$

Performing the integration and collecting terms yields in this case the following expression:

$$\frac{1}{q_1} \lim_{T \to \infty} \left\{ p_1 \cos \omega t + \frac{1}{\omega} \sin \omega t - \frac{1}{\omega} \sin \omega T \right\}.$$

This has a sine and a cosine term, both of which are independent of T, and which may be equated to $G_1 \cos \omega t$ and $G_2 \sin \omega t$. This indeed yields the results found previously and listed in Table 2.2, but there is also a constant, which depends on T and which does not even approach a definite limit as $T \to \infty$. This is a "transient" that never dies out, indicating that at present, at a fixed time t, the strain still depends on the point within a period at which long, long ago the oscillating load was started. A term of this kind is to be expected whenever the spring-dashpot model has a free dashpot, that is, in all fluids. For these materials, $\epsilon = \text{const}$ is a solution of the homogeneous differential equation $\mathbf{Q}\epsilon = 0$, and this constant may appear in addition to the particular solution (5.10a).

We now reverse our problem: Can we find the creep compliance $J(t)$ when the complex compliance $G(\omega)$ is known? To find the answer, we need a simple formula from the theory of the Fourier integral [21, 22]. It says that the unit step function can be written in the form

$$\Delta(t) = \frac{1}{2} + \frac{1}{\pi} \int_0^\infty \frac{\sin \omega t}{\omega} \, d\omega. \tag{5.23}$$

The second term on the right-hand side is a function of t and changes sign when t is replaced by $-t$. The equation states that, for $t > 0$, it has the constant value $1/2$.

The creep compliance $J(t)$ is the strain produced by a unit of stress applied as a step function, $\sigma = \Delta(t)$. Equation (5.23) shows how this stress may be resolved into an average of $\sigma = 1/2$ and the sum of infinitely many oscillations of infinitesimal amplitudes $d\omega/\pi\omega$. To these latter ones we may apply (5.10b) to find the corresponding strain, but we have still to find a way to deal with the constant average $\sigma = 1/2$. To make (5.10) applicable to it, we interpret it as a cosine oscillation of vanishing frequency,

$$\tfrac{1}{2} \equiv \tfrac{1}{2} \lim_{\omega \to 0} \cos \omega t.$$

Equation (5.10a) then yields

$$\epsilon(t) = \tfrac{1}{2} \lim_{\omega \to 0} [G_1(\omega) \cos \omega t - G_2(\omega) \sin \omega t]$$
$$+ \frac{1}{\pi} \int_0^\infty [G_1(\omega) \sin \omega t + G_2(\omega) \cos \omega t] \frac{d\omega}{\omega}, \quad (5.24)$$

and this must be equal to $J(t)$. In the first term of the first bracket the limiting process may at once be carried out, and in the second term we may at least let $\sin \omega t \approx \omega t$. We then have

$$J(t) = \tfrac{1}{2} G_1(0) + \frac{1}{\pi} \int_0^\infty G_2(\omega) \cos \omega t \frac{d\omega}{\omega}$$
$$- \tfrac{1}{2} t \lim_{\omega \to 0} [\omega G_2(\omega)] + \frac{1}{\pi} \int_0^\infty G_1(\omega) \sin \omega t \frac{d\omega}{\omega}. \quad (5.25)$$

In this equation terms have been so arranged that the first line is an even function of t and the second an odd one. Now consider any $t < 0$. Since then $J(t) = 0$, it follows that the two lines are equal in absolute value, but opposite in sign. When we now change the sign of t to positive, all that happens is that the second line changes sign, and then both lines are equal and each of them equals $\tfrac{1}{2} J(t)$. Thus we obtain two formulas for the creep compliance, namely:

$$J(t) = G_1(0) + \frac{2}{\pi} \int_0^\infty G_2(\omega) \cos \omega t \frac{d\omega}{\omega} \quad (5.26a)$$

and

$$J(t) = -t \lim_{w \to 0} [\omega G_2(\omega)] + \frac{2}{\pi} \int_0^\infty G_1(\omega) \sin \omega t \frac{d\omega}{\omega}. \quad (5.26b)$$

As we have seen, a sinusoidal stress may produce a strain which, in addition to $\sin \omega t$ and $\cos \omega t$ contains an additive constant $\epsilon = c$ of undefined value. Thus the right-hand side of (5.25) may not represent $J(t)$ but rather $J(t) + c$.

Since this constant is an even function of t, it would be part of the first line and hence would appear in (5.26a). We must therefore expect that (5.26b) is correct while (5.26a) may be in error by a constant.

For a viscous fluid we find from Table 2.2 that $G_1 \equiv 0$, $G_2 = -1/q_1\omega$. This we now introduce into (5.26a) and have

$$J(t) = -\frac{2}{\pi q_1} \int_0^\infty \cos \omega t \frac{d\omega}{\omega^2} = -\frac{2t}{\pi q_1} \int_0^\infty \frac{\cos \omega t \, d(\omega t)}{(\omega t)^2}.$$

This integral leads to a rare transcendental function, the sine integral, defined by the formula

$$\mathrm{Si}\, x = \int_0^x \frac{\sin y}{y} \, dy.$$

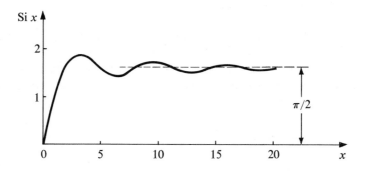

FIGURE 5.3. *Sine integral* Si x.

It has been tabulated and is shown in Figure 5.3. An integration by parts brings our integral in a suitable form and we find easily that

$$J(t) = -\frac{2t}{\pi q_1}\left[-\frac{\cos \omega t}{\omega t} - \mathrm{Si}\,(\omega t)\right]_0^\infty = -\frac{2}{\pi q_1}\left(\infty - \frac{\pi t}{2}\right),$$

a meaningless result. We try now (5.26b) and find very easily

$$J(t) = -t \lim_{\omega \to 0}\left(-\frac{1}{q_1}\right) = \frac{t}{q_1},$$

which is correct. The Maxwell fluid may be handled in a similar way. For other materials the integrals are difficult and require complex contour integration. For readers sufficiently experienced in complex variable theory we use the Kelvin solid to demonstrate the technique.

We insert G_1 and G_2 from Table 2.2 into (5.26a).

$$J(t) = \frac{1}{q_0} - \frac{2q_1}{\pi} \int_0^\infty \frac{\cos \omega t}{q_0^2 + q_1^2 \omega^2} \, d\omega$$

$$= \frac{1}{q_0} - \frac{2t}{\pi q_1} \int_0^\infty \frac{\cos \omega t}{(\lambda t)^2 + (\omega t)^2} \, d(\omega t).$$

We must find the integral

$$H = \int_0^\infty \frac{\cos z \, dz}{a^2 + z^2},$$

and when we interpret $z = x + iy$ as a complex variable, our integration path is the positive part of the real axis (Figure 5.4). Since the integrand is an even function, the integral over the entire real axis is $2H$, and this does not

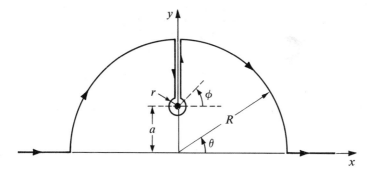

FIGURE 5.4. *Complex contour integral.*

change even when we add an integral over an odd function which, by itself, equals zero:

$$2H = \int_{-\infty}^\infty \frac{\cos z \, dz}{a^2 + z^2} + i \int_{-\infty}^\infty \frac{\sin z \, dz}{a^2 + z^2} = \int_{-\infty}^\infty \frac{e^{iz} \, dz}{a^2 + z^2}.$$

In the theory of complex variables it is shown that an integral does not change its value if we change the integration path (connecting the same end points), provided that there is no singular point of the integrand between the two paths (Cauchy's integral theorem). This condition is satisfied when we switch to the path which in Figure 5.4 is shown by a heavy line. It consists of the outer parts of the real axis and a large half-circle, but this half-circle is interrupted by a detour, which is so chosen that the singular point $z = ia$ (for which $a^2 + z^2 = 0$) still lies above the integration path. The vertical parts of this detour are supposed to coincide with the y axis. For both, the integrand is the same, but going down, dy is negative, and going up, it is positive, and the contributions to $2H$ cancel each other. On the big circle we write $z = Re^{i\theta}$ and on the small one $z = ia + re^{i\phi}$. When we let $R \to \infty$, the horizontal parts of the path vanish entirely, and we have ultimately

$$2H = \lim_{R \to \infty} \int_{\pi}^{0} \frac{\exp(iRe^{i\theta})}{a^2 + R^2 e^{2i\theta}} Rie^{i\theta}\, d\theta + \lim_{r \to 0} \int_{\pi/2}^{5\pi/2} \frac{\exp i(ia + re^{i\phi})}{a^2 + (ia + re^{i\phi})^2} rie^{i\phi}\, d\phi.$$

Now let us have a close look at the first integral. In the numerator we write

$$\exp(iRe^{i\theta}) = e^{iR(\cos\theta + i\sin\theta)} = e^{iR\cos\theta}e^{-R\sin\theta}$$
$$= [\cos(R\cos\theta) + i\sin(R\cos\theta)]e^{-R\sin\theta}.$$

When $R \to \infty$, the factor in the brackets is bounded and the real exponential behind it tends to zero. In addition, the integrand has another R, but it also has an R^2 in the denominator and therefore tends to zero. Then only the integral over the little circle is left, and we proceed as follows:

$$2H = \lim_{r \to 0} \int_{\pi/2}^{5\pi/2} \frac{e^{-a}e^{ir\cos\phi}e^{-r\sin\phi}}{a^2 - a^2 + 2iare^{i\phi} + r^2 e^{2i\phi}} rie^{i\phi}\, d\phi$$
$$= ie^{-a} \lim_{r \to 0} \int_{\pi/2}^{5\pi/2} \frac{e^{ir\cos\phi}e^{-r\sin\phi}}{2ia + re^{i\phi}}\, d\phi.$$

In the numerator each factor approaches in the limit $e^0 = 1$, and in the denominator the second term vanishes. The integrand is then a constant, and we arrive at the result

$$H = \frac{1}{2}\frac{e^{-a}}{2a} \cdot 2\pi = \frac{\pi}{2a}e^{-a}.$$

This we now apply to our original problem with $z = \omega t$, $a = \lambda t = q_0 t/q_1$ to obtain

$$J(t) = \frac{1}{q_0} - \frac{2t}{\pi q_1} \cdot \frac{\pi q_1}{2q_0 t}e^{-q_0 t/q_1} = \frac{1}{q_0}(1 - e^{-q_0 t/q_1}),$$

which is the correct result. It is suggested that the reader try to use (5.26b) in a similar way. This is more difficult, since an additional singularity at $z = 0$ turns up that needs special handling. The result confirms without further incident the one just obtained.

With this example we terminate our study of the oscillatory behavior of viscoelastic materials and now turn our attention to vibrations of mechanical systems endowed with mass and containing a viscoelastic spring.

5.5. The Simple Spring-Mass System

Figure 5.5a shows the prototype of all oscillators of one degree of freedom: a mass M connected by a spring to a fixpoint. However, our spring is not elastic, but is a viscoelastic bar of cross section A. The displacement u of the mass is measured from a positon in which the system had been at rest before the vibration began.

To find the possible motions of the system, we have three equations, the dynamic equation

$$M\ddot{u} + F = 0, \tag{5.27a}$$

a kinematic relation

$$\epsilon = u/l \tag{5.27b}$$

and the constitutive equation of the spring material. Postulating an oscillatory motion

$$u = u_0 e^{i\omega t}, \tag{5.28}$$

we use the form (5.6).

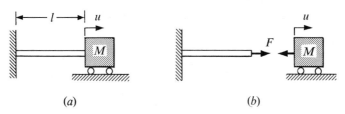

(a) (b)

FIGURE 5.5. *Simple oscillator.*

From (5.27) we derive

$$\epsilon = \frac{u_0}{l} e^{i\omega t}, \qquad A\sigma = F = -M\ddot{u} = Mu_0\omega^2 e^{i\omega t},$$

hence

$$\epsilon_0 = u_0/l, \qquad \sigma_0 = Mu_0\omega^2/A.$$

When this is introduced into (5.6), the complex amplitude u_0 drops out and we have

$$\omega^2 G(\omega) = \frac{A}{Ml}. \tag{5.29}$$

This is the frequency equation of our oscillator. For all truly viscoelastic materials (excluding the limiting case of the elastic solid), $G(\omega)$ is complex valued for real ω, and, therefore, (5.29) cannot have real solutions. This was to be expected, since an oscillator containing a viscoelastic element cannot make undamped vibrations.

Let us consider a few examples. For a Maxwell material we have

$$G(\omega) = \frac{p_1}{q_1} - \frac{i}{q_1\omega}$$

and hence the frequency equation

$$\frac{1}{q_1}(p_1\omega^2 - i\omega) = \frac{A}{Ml}.$$

This is a quadratic equation for ω and it has the roots

$$\omega = \frac{i}{2p_1} \pm \sqrt{\frac{Aq_1}{Mlp_1} - \frac{1}{4p_1^2}}.$$

If the mass is small or the spring stiff (large $E_0 = q_1/p_1$), the root has a real value, let us say $=\nu$, and we have

$$i\omega = -\frac{1}{2p_1} \pm i\nu,$$

hence

$$u = e^{-t/2p_1}(C_1 e^{i\nu t} + C_2 e^{-i\nu t}) = e^{-t/2p_1}(B_1 \cos \nu t + B_2 \sin \nu t).$$

This is a damped vibration.

If the mass is large or the spring soft, the square root will be imaginary, let us say $=i\nu$, and we have

$$i\omega = -\frac{1}{2p_1} \pm \nu = -\omega_{1,2}, \qquad \omega_{1,2} > 0,$$

and

$$u = C_1 e^{-\omega_1 t} + C_2 e^{-\omega_2 t},$$

that is, the case of aperiodic damping, as known from vibration theory. Our system, however, is not the one commonly used to study a damped oscillator (see Exercise 5.1).

If the spring is made of a three-parameter solid, we arrive at an interesting paradox. From the last two columns of Table 2.2 we extract

$$G(\omega) = \frac{q_0 + p_1 q_1 \omega^2}{q_0^2 + q_1^2 \omega^2} - i \frac{(q_1 - q_0 p_1)\omega}{q_0^2 + q_1^2 \omega^2},$$

and when we introduce this into the frequency equation (5.29) and multiply by the common denominator, we obtain a fourth-degree equation for ω:

$$(q_0 + p_1 q_1 \omega^2)\omega^2 - i(q_1 - q_0 p_1)\omega^3 - \frac{A}{Ml}(q_0^2 + q_1^2 \omega^2) = 0. \qquad (5.30a)$$

It has four roots, and this makes us expect that there are four different modes of vibration. However, if we use (5.7) to calculate $G(\omega)$, we find

$$G(\omega) = \frac{1 + p_1 i\omega}{q_0 + q_1 i\omega},$$

and when this is inserted into (5.29), the resulting equation is only of the third degree:

$$(1 + p_1 i\omega)\omega^2 - \frac{A}{Ml}(q_0 + q_1 i\omega) = 0. \qquad (5.30b)$$

We must conclude that either in (5.30b) we have missed something, or that (5.30a) contains an extraneous root. The latter is true. G_1 and G_2 are defined by the third member of (5.7). They were meant to be the real and imaginary parts of G, and this is the case as long as ω is real. The splitting of G into the two parts was achieved by multiplying the numerator and the denominator of the fraction in (5.7) by $\Sigma q_k(-i)^k\omega^k$. This increases the degree of the numerator (in this case by one), and the ω that makes this factor vanish is the root which (5.30a) has and (5.30b) does not have. It has nothing to do with the mechanical problem.

Instead of using the frequency equation (5.29) to find the possible motions of the oscillator, we might equally well formulate its differential equation and then solve it. To do this, we use again (5.27), but as the constitutive equation of the material we now use the differential equation (2.23c). On its right side we introduce ϵ from (5.27b) and on the left

$$\sigma = \frac{F}{A} = -\frac{M}{A}\ddot{u}$$

from (5.27a) to obtain the equation

$$-\frac{M}{A}\mathbf{P}(\ddot{u}) = \frac{1}{l}\mathbf{Q}(u). \tag{5.31}$$

Since $\mathbf{P}$ is an operator of the mth order, and since the order of $\mathbf{Q}$ is $n < m + 2$, (5.31) is a differential equation of $(m + 2)$nd order. Upon inspecting the differential equations in Table 2.2, we see that for the viscous fluid and the Kelvin solid the problem is of the second order, exactly as for an elastic spring; that for the Maxwell fluid, both three-parameter materials, and the four-parameter solid it is of the third order; and for the four-parameter fluid, it is of the fourth order. A unique solution requires a corresponding number of initial conditions, and we ask where we may find them. As in every problem of dynamics, the initial values of u and $\dot{u}$ should certainly be known, but what else should be known, and why?

We find the key to an answer when we inspect the simplest case, the Maxwell spring. Figure 5.6 shows the oscillator in three positions, the Maxwell bar being replaced by the proper model. In Figure 5.6a the system is in the undisturbed position. The state of Figure 5.6b can be obtained by pulling the mass very suddenly down. Then the dashpot has had no time to deform, and the spring is stretched. When the mass is held just long enough to make sure that $\dot{u} = 0$ and then released, a vibration will ensue which begins like an elastic vibration, the dashpot deforming as time permits and gradually draining energy from the system.

The system of Figure 5.6a may be brought in the state of Figure 5.6c by pulling the mass down very slowly. Then almost no force is needed and the entire deformation comes from the dashpot. When we again make sure that $\dot{u} = 0$ and then release the mass, nothing will happen. The oscillator is in a state of equilibrium, and it will remain there.

In both cases we have at $t = 0$ the initial conditions $u = u_0$ and $\dot{u} = 0$, and the difference lies in the position of the internal joint between the spring and the dashpot. If we know this, we know enough to choose the correct motion among the solutions of the differential equation. In an actual viscoelastic material, however, there is no spring and no dashpot, and a statement

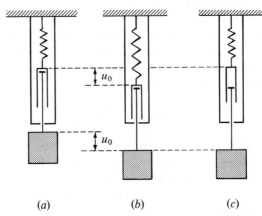

(a)   (b)   (c)

FIGURE 5.6. *Simple oscillator with a Maxwell spring.*

about the internal joint is not available. We must then formulate the difference between the two initial states in terms of the acceleration $\ddot{u}$. In the case of Figure 5.6b, the sudden strain $\epsilon_0 = u_0/l$ leads to a stress $\sigma_0 = E_0\epsilon_0$ and hence to an acceleration $\ddot{u} = E_0 A\epsilon_0/M$. In Figure 5.6c, there is no force at all and hence $\ddot{u} = 0$. Which of the two conditions applies depends on what has been done to the system before the vibration started, and there are, of course, infinitely many possibilities to produce different starting values of $\ddot{u}$.

On p. 69 the materials have been enumerated that lead to a third-order or a fourth-order equation, and if we now check in Table 2.2 the corresponding models, we see that for the third-order problems they have one internal joint and that the four-parameter fluid has two.

5.6. Forced Vibrations

As we have seen, the free vibrations of a viscoelastic oscillator are damped, that is, the solution ω of the frequency equation (5.29) is always complex with a positive imaginary part. We shall now apply to the same mass an external force

$$P = P_0 e^{i\omega_0 t}$$

with an arbitrary, real frequency ω_0 (Figure 5.7). The amplitude P_0 of this "driving force" may be complex, that is, the real part of P may contain a sine as well as a cosine.

The presence of this force modifies the dynamic equation (5.27a), which now reads

$$M\ddot{u} + F = P_0 e^{i\omega_0 t}. \tag{5.32}$$

When we combine this equation with (5.27b) and (2.23c), we arrive at a differential equation, which is the inhomogeneous counterpart to (5.31). The

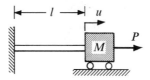

FIGURE 5.7. *Forced vibration of a simple oscillator.*

free vibrations studied before are its complementary solution, and besides this it has a particular solution of the form

$$u = u_0 e^{i\omega_0 t}.$$

It describes the steady state that develops after the free vibrations have died down. At present we are interested only in this solution. With this in mind, we may bypass the differential equation and combine (5.32) with (5.27b) and (5.6). After dropping a factor $e^{i\omega_0 t}$, (5.27b) and (5.32) yield

$$\epsilon_0 = u_0/l, \qquad A\sigma_0 = Mu_0\omega_0^2 + P_0,$$

and upon introducing this into (5.6) we find

$$\frac{u_0}{l} = \frac{G(\omega_0)}{A}(Mu_0\omega_0^2 + P_0),$$

which may be solved for the displacement amplitude

$$u_0 = \frac{P_0 l G(\omega_0)}{A - Ml\omega_0^2 G(\omega_0)}.$$

Because of (5.29), this may be written in the form

$$u_0 = \frac{P_0}{M} \frac{G(\omega_0)}{\omega^2 G(\omega) - \omega_0^2 G(\omega_0)}. \tag{5.33a}$$

The velocity

$$\dot{u} = v = v_0 e^{i\omega_0 t}$$

has the amplitude

$$v_0 = \frac{iP_0}{M} \frac{\omega_0 G(\omega_0)}{\omega^2 G(\omega) - \omega_0^2 G(\omega_0)}. \qquad (5.33b)$$

We describe the response of an oscillator to a periodic driving force by its *admittance*, which is the amplitude of the velocity per unit of driving force:

$$\mathscr{A} = \mathscr{A}_1 + i\mathscr{A}_2 = \frac{v_0}{P_0} = \frac{1}{M} \frac{i\omega_0 G(\omega_0)}{\omega^2 G(\omega) - \omega_0^2 G(\omega_0)}. \qquad (5.34)$$

The reciprocal of this quantity, the force needed per unit of velocity, is known as the *impedance* or *complex resistance* of the oscillator. When actually splitting a given $\mathscr{A}$ into its real and imaginary parts, the reader should note that ω is complex, but that the expression $\omega^2 G(\omega)$ is real.

Exercises

5.1. Assume that the spring in Figure 5.5 obeys the Kelvin law. Formulate the frequency equation and discuss its solution.

5.2. A torsion bar (Figure 5.8) consists of a viscoelastic core and an elastic outer shell. The stress-strain laws are

$$\text{for the core:} \qquad \tau + p_1 \dot{\tau} = q_1 \dot{\gamma},$$
$$\text{for the shell:} \qquad \tau = G\gamma.$$

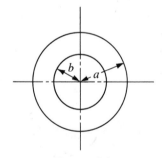

FIGURE 5.8.

An oscillating torque $M_t = M_0 e^{i\omega t}$ is applied. Calculate the complex compliance defined by the relation

$$\theta = M_0 G(\omega) e^{i\omega t},$$

where θ is the twist of the bar.

5.3. A viscoelastic beam (Figure 5.9) is simply supported at both ends and has at the midspan point a mass m attached to it. The mass of the beam is negligible. The beam material is characterized by its complex compliance $G(\omega)$. Find the natural frequency of the system. Calculate the forced vibrations

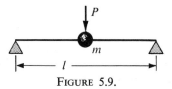

FIGURE 5.9.

caused by the load $P = P_0 e^{i\omega t}$. Calculate the impedance of the system and plot it as a function of the frequency ω of the driving force, using any one of the materials listed in Table 2.2.

5.4. The beam shown in Figure 5.10 is made of a viscoelastic material and rests on two viscoelastic springs. The beam material is described by the relation $\mathbf{P}_a(\sigma) = \mathbf{Q}_a(\epsilon)$ and the springs by $\mathbf{P}_b(R) = \mathbf{Q}_b(\delta)$, where R is the reaction of the support and δ the deflection of the spring under this force.

At the midspan point a mass m is attached that is large enough to permit neglecting the mass of the beam. Find the frequency equation for lateral vibrations of the beam.

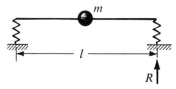

FIGURE 5.10.

For a numerical evaluation the following special case may be considered: beam: a three-parameter solid, constants

$$q_{0a} = q_0, \qquad p_{1a} = p_1, \qquad q_{1a} = 3q_0 p_1;$$

springs: Kelvin law,

$$q_{0b} = 5lq_0, \qquad q_{1b} = 5lq_0 p_1.$$

REFERENCES

The complex compliance and its reciprocal, the complex modulus, may be found in many papers, e.g. [1], p. 463, and

[19] E. H. LEE, "Stress Analysis in Viscoelastic Materials," *J. Appl. Phys.*, **27** (1956), 665–672.

The relations between the different compliances and the relaxation modulus are discussed in the following monograph:

[20] B. GROSS, *Mathematical Structure of the Theories of Viscoelasticity* (Paris: Hermann, 1953).

Equation (5.23) can easily be derived from the basic principles of the Fourier integral. It may be found at the following places:

[21] G. A. KORN and T. M. KORN, *Mathematical Handbook for Scientists and Engineers* (New York: McGraw-Hill, 1961), p. 29.9–2, eq. (21.9–8). (Note a slight change in the integration domain.)

[22] A. PAPOULIS, *The Fourier Integral and Its Applications* (New York: McGraw-Hill, 1962), p. 39.

The definition of the sine integral may be found in reference [21], p. 21.3–1, eq. (21.3–1). For more detail consult

[23] W. FLÜGGE, *Four-Place Tables of Transcendental Functions* (London: Pergamon, 1954), pp. 115–116, 131, 133. (Contains the basic formulas needed for using the sine integral and a table of numerical values.)

The Cauchy theorem is one of the fundamental theorems of complex variable theory and may be found in all texts on the subject, for example:

[24] R. V. CHURCHILL, *Complex Variables and Applications* (2nd ed.) (New York: McGraw-Hill, 1960), pp. 106–111. (There this theorem is called the Cauchy-Goursat theorem.)

[25] C. R. WYLIE, ref. [8], p. 561.

CHAPTER 6

Axial Impact

T HE SUBJECT OF THIS CHAPTER is a straight cylindrical bar that begins at $x = 0$ and extends to infinity. At the end of the bar we wish either to apply suddenly a tensile or compressive force or to enforce an axial displacement. For an elastic bar it is well known [26] that any sudden action at its end produces a stress wave that runs at a definite speed c and that carries with it a discontinuity in stress and in velocity. We shall study the corresponding phenomenon for a viscoelastic bar.

6.1. The Differential Equation

This bar is shown in Figure 6.1a. Its cross section has the area A and may have any compact shape. Since there will be only axial forces, displacements u occur only in axial direction. Dots will indicate time derivatives, and primes, derivatives with respect to x.

In Figure 6.1b a bar element is shown. At its left end the axial force $N = A\sigma$ is acting, which is a function of x and t. The force at the right end is therefore $N + N' dx$, and the difference between these forces produces an acceleration $\ddot{u}$ of the element of mass $\rho A\, dx = \mu\, dx$, where ρ is the mass density of the material and μ is the mass per unit length of the bar. This yields the dynamic equation

$$\mu\ddot{u} = N'. \qquad (6.1)$$

If at a certain time the displacement of the left end is u and that of the right end $u + u'\, dx$, then the strain, that is, the difference between the two divided by the length dx of the element, is

$$\epsilon = u'. \qquad (6.2)$$

75

This is the kinematic relation. As the constitutive relation we use (2.23b), which we multiply at once by A to obtain

$$\sum_0^m p_k \frac{\partial^k N}{\partial t^k} = A \sum_0^n q_k \frac{\partial^k u'}{\partial t^k} . \tag{6.3}$$

In this equation we have already made use of (6.2). We differentiate it once more with respect to x and then use (6.1) to express N' by $\ddot{u}$:

$$\frac{\mu}{A} \sum_0^m p_k \frac{\partial^{k+2} u}{\partial t^{k+2}} - \sum_0^n q_k \frac{\partial^{k+2} u}{\partial x^2 \partial t^k} = 0. \tag{6.4}$$

This is the differential equation of our problem, a partial differential equation for the displacement u.

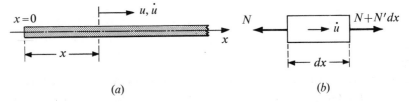

FIGURE 6.1. *Viscoelastic bar—a: the bar; b: element.*

For all materials listed in Table 2.2, there is either $m = n$ or $m = n - 1$. In both cases (6.4) is of order $n + 2$. If $m = n$, there are two terms of order $n + 2$, the highest one occurring. They are the second space and time derivatives of $\partial^n u/\partial t^n$, and since all coefficients $p_k, q_k > 0$, the minus sign in (6.4) indicates that our equation is of the hyperbolic type, that is, that it describes a wave propagation phenomenon [36–39].

If $m = n - 1$, there is only one term of order $n + 2$, and (6.4) is of the parabolic type, like the heat equation. In this case there are no waves of finite velocity.

As we have seen on p. 19, the materials for which $m = n$ are those which have an impact modulus $E_0 = q_n/p_n$.

6.2. The Wave Front

For the study of the propagation of waves, the impulse-momentum theorem yields a very important tool. Although (6.6) can be derived from the differential equation and therefore does not represent new physical information, it is easier to derive it directly from basic mechanical principles.

When we speak of waves in this context, we do not mean anything oscillatory, but rather a sharp discontinuity in stress or velocity, or any other mechanical quantity, traveling along the bar at a finite speed c. We consider

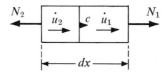

FIGURE 6.2. *Bar element with wave front.*

now an element dx of the bar which contains such a moving discontinuity or *wave front* (Figure 6.2). Before the wave front, the axial force and the velocity are N_1, $\dot{u}_1$; and behind it they are N_2, $\dot{u}_2$. The differences

$$\Delta N = N_2 - N_1, \qquad \Delta \dot{u} = \dot{u}_2 - \dot{u}_1 \qquad (6.5)$$

are finite quantities describing the intensity of the wave front.

Before the wave front enters the element from the left, the velocity of all points is $\dot{u}_1$ and the forces at both ends differ at most by an infinitesimal amount. After the wave front has left, near-equilibrium has again been restored, but the velocity is now $\dot{u}_2$. During the time $dt = dx/c$, which the wave front needed to pass through the element, the forces were in unbalance and produced an impulse $(N_1 - N_2)\, dt = -\Delta N\, dt$, which is responsible for the increase in momentum $\mu\, dx \cdot \Delta \dot{u}$. The impulse-momentum theorem states that

$$\mu\, dx\, \Delta \dot{u} = -\Delta N\, dt,$$

whence

$$\Delta \dot{u} = -\frac{1}{\mu c} \Delta N. \qquad (6.6)$$

The quantity μc is the force step needed to produce a unit step in velocity. It is called the *impedance* or *wave resistance* of the bar.

In an x, t plane, a wave front traveling with the constant speed c is represented by a straight line (Figure 6.3). This wave line separates a space-time

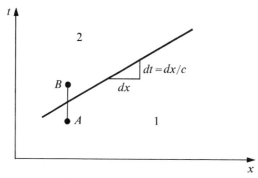

FIGURE 6.3. *Wave propagation in the x, t-plane.*

region 1 from a region 2. For a fixed x, region 1 represents the time before the wave front passes; for a fixed time t, it contains that part of the bar where the wave front has not yet been. Certain quantities, like the jump ΔN of the axial force or $\Delta \dot{u}$ of the velocity, are defined only on the wave front, that is, on the boundary between the regions 1 and 2. Consequently, they have only a derivative along this line.

For any function $f(x, t)$, we may write the difference df of its values for two adjacent points as

$$df = f' \, dx + \dot{f} \, dt.$$

In particular, if both points are on a wave line, we have $dt = dx/c$ and hence

$$df = \left(f' + \frac{1}{c} \dot{f} \right) dx.$$

Since the coordinates x and t do not have the same dimension, there is no such thing as a line element on the wave line. We therefore cannot form a differential quotient by dividing df by such a line element, but must resort to using either dx or dt to measure the distance of these points. We decide arbitrarily for x and write

$$\frac{df}{dx} \equiv \frac{Df}{Dx} = f' + \frac{1}{c} \dot{f}. \tag{6.7}$$

We shall use D to keep reminded that Dx is not the distance between the x, t points compared, but only a standardized measure for it.

Since the bar does not fall apart, the displacement u must be a continuous function of x and t, and even on the wave front there is

$$\Delta u = u_2 - u_1 \equiv 0.$$

Differentiating this identity along the wave line, we see that

$$\frac{D\Delta u}{Dx} = \Delta u' + \frac{1}{c} \Delta \dot{u} = 0,$$

whence

$$\Delta u = -c \, \Delta u'. \tag{6.8}$$

We may combine this with the momentum equation (6.6) to find that

$$\Delta u' = \frac{1}{\mu c^2} \Delta N. \tag{6.9}$$

This may be interpretated as a relation between strain and stress, which does not depend on the constitutive law.

When this law, (6.3) is introduced, we arrive at a formula for the wave velocity c. The procedure is as follows: The differential equation (6.3) is integrated with respect to t, starting from a fixed point below the wave line and ending at a variable point below or above it. Any term of the sums in (6.3) is then a function of the upper integration limit and may again be integrated. This operation is repeated to a total of n integrations and the limits of the last integral are the points A and B in Figure 6.3. Most of the terms are then continuous functions of the t values at A and B. When we now let A and B approach the wave line, these integrals vanish.

There are two exceptions to this statement. The highest term on the right yields after n integrations

$$\lim_{A \to B} \int_A^B \frac{\partial u'}{\partial t} \, dt = \lim_{A \to B} (u'_B - u'_A) = \Delta u',$$

and if, but only if, $m = n$, also the highest term on the left makes a non-vanishing contribution:

$$\lim_{A \to B} \int_A^B \frac{\partial N}{\partial t} \, dt = \lim_{A \to B} (N_B - N_A) = \Delta N,$$

and there results the relation

$$p_n \, \Delta N = A q_n \, \Delta u'. \tag{6.10}$$

If $m < n$, then $p_n = 0$, and the same relation holds true, but its left-hand side is zero.

When we now compare (6.9) and (6.10), we see that

$$c^2 = \frac{A q_n}{\mu p_n}. \tag{6.11a}$$

With $\mu = A\rho$ and $q_n/p_n = E_0$ equal to the impact modulus, we may write our result also in the form

$$c^2 = E_0/\rho. \tag{6.11b}$$

Evidently, a finite wave velocity exists only in materials which have an impact modulus E_0. In other materials $p_n = 0$ leads to $c = \infty$.

In an infinite elastic bar, a wave once set in motion propagates without change in form or intensity. In a viscoelastic material we must expect that the wave front loses intensity as it travels. To find out what really happens, we go back to the impulse-momentum equation (6.6) and differentiate it along the wave line:

$$-\frac{D\Delta \dot{u}}{Dx} = \frac{1}{\mu c} \frac{D\Delta N}{Dx} = \frac{1}{\mu c} \Delta N' + \frac{1}{\mu c^2} \Delta \dot{N}.$$

When we still apply (6.1) to N', we may bring this into the following form:

$$\frac{D\Delta\dot{u}}{Dx} + \frac{1}{c}\Delta\ddot{u} + \frac{1}{\mu c^2}\Delta\dot{N} = 0. \tag{6.12}$$

We shall later make out of it a differential equation for $\Delta\dot{u}$. To do so, we need the viscoelastic law of the material.

6.3. Maxwell Material

The Maxwell material is defined by the relation

$$p_1\dot{\sigma} + \sigma = q_1\dot{\epsilon}. \tag{6.13}$$

Although its long-range behavior characterizes it as a fluid, it does have initial elasticity and therefore permits stress waves of finite velocity

$$c = \sqrt{q_1/\rho p_1}. \tag{6.14}$$

To find the law of decay of the step height of a wave, we must introduce information drawn from (6.13) into (6.12). To begin with, we write (6.13) for two adjacent points like A and B in Figure 6.3 and form the difference (in other words, we apply the Δ operator to this equation). The result is

$$p_1\,\Delta\dot{\sigma} = -\Delta\sigma + q_1\,\Delta\dot{\epsilon}.$$

Multiplying by A and using (6.6) and (6.2) on the right-hand side, we may write this as

$$p_1\,\Delta\dot{N} = \mu c\,\Delta\dot{u} + Aq_1\,\Delta\dot{u}',$$

and this may now be introduced in the last term of (6.12) to yield

$$\frac{D\Delta\dot{u}}{Dx} + \frac{1}{c}\Delta\ddot{u} + \frac{1}{p_1 c}\Delta\dot{u} + \frac{Aq_1}{p_1\mu c^2}\Delta\dot{u}' = 0.$$

Because of (6.11a), the coefficient of the last term equals unity, and the second and fourth terms can be combined into $D\Delta\dot{u}/Dx$, so that we arrive at a first-order differential equation for the velocity step:

$$2\frac{D\Delta\dot{u}}{Dx} + \frac{1}{p_1 c}\Delta\dot{u} = 0. \tag{6.15}$$

It has the solution

$$\Delta\dot{u} = Ce^{-x/2p_1 c}. \tag{6.16a}$$

According to (6.6), this discontinuity in the velocity is accompanied by a step in the axial force

$$\Delta N = -C\mu c e^{-x/2p_1 c}. \tag{6.16b}$$

Both decay as the wave moves on toward increasing x.

Of course, a wave front may also move from right to left. In this case the wave velocity is negative and all our formulas apply to such waves as well.

To obtain further information about stress and motion of the bar, we must solve (6.4). For the Maxwell material it reads

$$\rho(\ddot{u} + p_1\dddot{u}) - q_1\ddot{u}'' = 0. \tag{6.17}$$

We wish to solve it for the case that for $t < 0$ the bar is at rest and free of stress and that for all $t > 0$ either u or N is prescribed at the end $x = 0$.

When (6.17) is subjected to the Laplace transformation, all the terms in (2.18) which contain initial values do not appear, and we have simply

$$q_1 s\bar{u}'' - \rho(p_1 s^3 + s^2)\bar{u} = 0. \tag{6.18}$$

Contrary to what is often said and written, this is a partial differential equation for a function $\bar{u}(x, s)$. However, it contains only a derivative with respect to x and therefore can be solved by familiar methods from the theory of ordinary differential equations. It is satisfied by

$$\bar{u} = B(x)e^{\lambda x} \tag{6.19a}$$

with

$$\lambda = \pm \frac{1}{c}\sqrt{s(s + 1/p_1)}. \tag{6.19b}$$

The positive value of λ, though acceptable for a solution of (6.18), must be rejected because every Laplace transform must, for $s \to \infty$, tend to zero. Mechanically speaking, this means that we are excluding waves running from right to left, since these would be incompatible with complete rest for $t < 0$. In fluid dynamics a similar exclusion is known as the "rule of forbidden signals" (no signals coming to us from $x = \infty$).

As might be expected of a solution of a partial differential equation, $\bar{u}(x, s)$ contains a free function $B(s)$, which we now shall determine from the initial condition. We choose the case that at $t = 0$ a constant tensile force is suddenly applied to the bar:

$$N(0, t) = P\,\Delta(t), \qquad \bar{N}(0, s) = Ps^{-1}. \tag{6.20}$$

Then the first element dx of the bar is exactly in the condition used for defining the creep compliance $J(t)$, and its strain is

$$\epsilon(0, t) = u'(0, t) = \frac{P}{A}J(t), \qquad \bar{u}'(0, s) = \frac{P}{A}\bar{J}(s). \tag{6.21}$$

This is our initial condition. For a Maxwell material we have

$$J(t) = \frac{p_1 + t}{q_1}, \qquad \bar{J}(s) = \frac{1}{q_1}\left(\frac{p_1}{s} + \frac{1}{s^2}\right)$$

and, therefore,

$$\bar{u}'(0, s) = \lambda B(s) = \frac{P}{Aq_1}\left(\frac{p_1}{s} + \frac{1}{s^2}\right).$$

From this equation we find $B(s)$ and hence the final form of $\bar{u}$:

$$\bar{u}(x, s) = -\frac{P}{\mu c}\frac{\sqrt{s + 1/p_1}}{s^2\sqrt{s}}\exp\left(-\frac{x}{c}\sqrt{s(s + 1/p_1)}\right). \qquad (6.22)$$

This must now be transformed back into the x, t plane.

We start from the transformation pair (7) in Table 2.1. As a first step, we let $a = i\alpha$ and introduce the modified Bessel function $I_0(x) = J_0(ix)$. This yields the pair

$$f(t) = I_0(\alpha\sqrt{t^2 - b^2}) \cdot \Delta(t - b),$$

$$\bar{f}(s) = \frac{1}{\sqrt{s^2 - \alpha^2}}\exp(-b\sqrt{s^2 - \alpha^2}).$$

Then we replace s by $(s + \alpha)$ in $\bar{f}$ and apply the shifting theorem [35], which says that the corresponding change of f is the appearance of a factor $e^{-\alpha t}$:

$$f(t) = I_0(\alpha\sqrt{t^2 - b^2})e^{-\alpha t}\Delta(t - b),$$

$$\bar{f}(s) = \frac{1}{\sqrt{s(s + 2\alpha)}}\exp(-b\sqrt{s(s + 2\alpha)}).$$

When we now let $2\alpha = 1/p_1$ and $b = x/c$, we have a pair that can be used with (6.22):

$$f_1(t) = I_0(\zeta)e^{-t/2p_1}\Delta(t - x/c),$$

$$\bar{f_1}(s) = \frac{1}{\sqrt{s(s + 1/p_1)}}\exp\left(-\frac{x}{c}\sqrt{s(s + 1/p_1)}\right),$$

where the abbreviation

$$\zeta = \frac{1}{2p_1}\sqrt{t^2 - x^2/c^2}$$

has been used. Another necessary pair is found by differentiating f_1:

$$\dot{f_1}(t) = f_2(t) = \frac{1}{2p_1}\left[-I_0(\zeta) + \frac{t}{2p_1\zeta}I_1(\zeta)\right]e^{-t/2p_1}\Delta(t - x/c),$$

$$\bar{f_2}(s) = \frac{s}{\sqrt{s(s + 1/p_1)}}\exp\left(-\frac{x}{c}\sqrt{s(s + 1/p_1)}\right).$$

With the last two pairs, we can handle the transformation of $s^2\bar{u}(x, s)$, which yields $\ddot{u}(x, t)$:

$$\ddot{u}(x, t) = -\frac{P}{\mu c}\left[\frac{1}{p_1}f_1(t) + f_2(t)\right]$$

$$= -\frac{P}{\mu c} \cdot \frac{1}{2p_1}\left[I_0(\zeta) + \frac{t}{2p_1\zeta}I_1(\zeta)\right]e^{-t/2p_1}, \qquad (6.23)$$

valid for $t > x/c$.

From (6.1) we find immediately N', and now we may calculate N, $\dot{u}$, and u by numerical integration. For N we have to integrate N' in x direction,

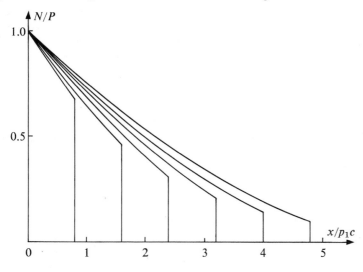

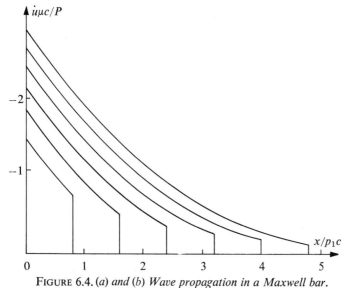

FIGURE 6.4. (*a*) *and* (*b*) *Wave propagation in a Maxwell bar.*

starting from the prescribed value $N(0, t) = P$, and for $\dot{u}$ and u we need two consecutive integrations in t direction starting at the wave front $x = ct$, where initial values are known. They are $u(x, ct^+) = 0$ and $\dot{u}(x, ct^+) = \Delta \dot{u}$ from (6.16a). The constant C in this equation follows from the fact that for $x = 0$, $t = 0^+$ the velocity is

$$\dot{u} = -P/\mu c,$$

as may be seen from (6.6).

Figure 6.4 shows the results of numerical work. The six curves in each diagram belong to values $t/p_1 = 0.8$, 1.6, 2.4, 3.2, 4.0, 4.8. Both diagrams show the presence of a wave front which runs at a constant velocity, and it may be seen how the step height decreases as the wave travels along the bar. In Figure 6.4a, the value of N at the left end is, of course, constant, and at any other point N jumps to a finite value when the wave front arrives and then continues to grow slowly, never reaching P.

For a positive (tensile) force P, the velocity $\dot{u}$ is necessarily negative. We have already seen that at the end of the bar it jumps to $-P/\mu c$ when the load is applied. Figure 6.4b shows that it keeps growing, in contrast to what happens in an elastic bar.

6.4. Viscous Material

In the limit $p_1 \to 0$ the Maxwell material degenerates into a viscous fluid. As may be seen from (6.14), the wave velocity c goes then to infinity. This means that there is no marked wave front and that every point of the bar "knows" at once when something is happening at the end. However, the product $c^2 p_1 = q_1/\rho$ remains finite, and this must be used when performing the limiting process.

This is most easily done on the Laplace transform $\bar{u}$, (6.22), writing

$$\bar{u}(x, s) = -\lim \frac{P}{A\rho c} \frac{\sqrt{p_1 s + 1}}{\sqrt{p_1}\, s^2 \sqrt{s}} \exp\left(-\frac{x}{c} \frac{\sqrt{s}\sqrt{p_1 s + 1}}{\sqrt{p_1}}\right)$$

$$= -\frac{P}{A\sqrt{\rho q_1}} \frac{1}{s^2 \sqrt{s}} \exp\left(-x\sqrt{\frac{\rho}{q_1}}\sqrt{s}\right). \tag{6.24}$$

This expression looks quite different from (6.22) and needs another transform pair. It is listed as (8) in Table 2.1 and yields in this case the velocity

$$\dot{u}(s, t) = -\frac{P}{A\sqrt{\rho q_1}}\left\{2\sqrt{\frac{t}{\pi}}\exp\left(-\frac{x^2 \rho}{4 q_1 t}\right) - x\sqrt{\frac{\rho}{q_1}}\left[1 - \operatorname{erf}\left(\frac{x}{2}\sqrt{\frac{\rho}{q_1 t}}\right)\right]\right\}. \tag{6.25}$$

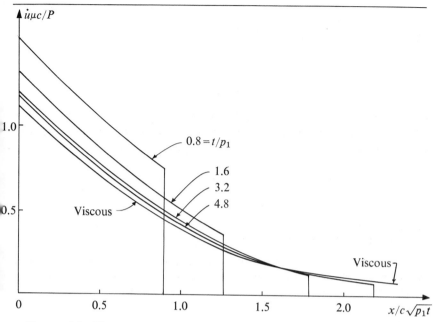

FIGURE 6.5. *Wave propagation, comparison of Maxwell fluid and viscous fluid.*

It is remarkable that in this case $\dot{u}/\sqrt{t}$ depends only on $x/\sqrt{t}$ and can be plotted over this variable as an abscissa. This has been done in Figure 6.5, and in this diagram the results from Figure 6.4b have been replotted. They yield, of course different curves for different t, and it may be seen how these curves gradually approach the unique one for the viscous bar: The more time that has elapsed since the wave front has passed at a certain point, the closer the behavior of the Maxwell bar approaches that of a viscous material.

Exercises

6.1. A tube of circular cross section is made of a viscoelastic material. It is filled with an incompressible, inviscid fluid of mass density ρ. In this fluid pressure waves can travel that are similar to the tension-compression waves in cylindrical rods. A theory of these waves can be formulated that parallels that of the rods. To obtain it, assume that the deformation of the tube in each cross section depends only on the local pressure p and not on the deformation of adjacent parts of the tube. Establish the differential equation, formulate the impulse-momentum equation, and find a formula for the wave velocity c.

6.2. The right end of a viscoelastic rod is connected to an elastic spring (spring stiffness k), which in turn is attached to a fixed abutment, Figure 6.6.

FIGURE 6.6.

A stress wave arrives from the left and will be partially reflected when it reaches the end. Write the proper end condition in terms of the displacement u. Assume that the bar is made of a three-parameter solid.

REFERENCES

A short outline of the theory of axial impact is found in

[26] S. TIMOSHENKO and J. N. GOODIER, *Theory of Elasticity* (2nd ed.) (New York: McGraw-Hill, 1951), pp. 438–452.

The presentation of the subject of viscoelastic impact in this book is based upon the author's work, done in 1944–1948 in Germany and France and, because of the world situation in those years, never published. The formalism used here has been developed in the following paper:

[27] W. FLÜGGE, "Die Ausbreitung von Biegewellen in Stäben," *Z. angew. Math. Mech.*, *22* (1942), 312–318.

The subject has found much attention in recent years. The following references [28] through [34] may be consulted for more detail:

[28] E. H. LEE and I. KANTER, "Wave Propagation in Finite Rods of Viscoelastic Material," *J. Appl. Phys.*, *24* (1953), 1115–1122. (Maxwell solid, includes reflection of the wave at the far end of the bar.)

[29] J. A. MORRISON, "Wave Propagation in Rods of Voigt Materials and Viscoelastic Materials with Three-Parameter Models," *Qu. Appl. Math.*, *14* (1956), 153–169.

[30] R. D. GLAUZ and E. H. LEE, "Transient Wave Analysis in a Linear Time-dependent Material," *J. Appl. Phys.*, *25* (1954), 947–953.

[31] E. H. LEE and J. A. MORRISON, "A Comparison of Longitudinal Waves in Rods of Viscoelastic Materials," *J. Polymer Sci.*, *19* (1956), 93–110. (Includes both three-parameter materials and the four-parameter fluid.)

[32] D. S. BERRY and S. C. HUNTER, "The Propagation of Dynamic Stresses in Viscoelastic Rods," *J. Mech. Phys. Solids*, *4* (1956), 72–95.

[33] S. C. HUNTER, "Viscoelastic Waves" in I. N. Sneddon and R. Hill (eds.), *Progress in Solid Mechanics*, (New York: Interscience, 1960), Vol. 1, pp. 1–57.

[34] W. FLÜGGE and J. R. HUTCHINSON, "Axial Vibrations of a Semiinfinite Viscoelastic Rod with External Constraint," *J. Acoust. Soc. Amer.*, *37* (1965), 14–18.

[35] The shifting theorem is (under various names) found in the following books: [4], p. 15, [5], p. 4, [6], p. 6, [7], p. 74.

The classification of partial differential equations of the second order in elliptic, parabolic, and hyperbolic equations is explained in texts on partial differential equations, for example:

[36] I. N. SNEDDON, *Elements of Partial Differential Equations*, (New York: McGraw-Hill, 1957), pp. 108, 118.

[37] F. B. HILDEBRAND, *Advanced Calculus for Applications* (Englewood Cliffs, N.J.: Prentice-Hall, 1948), p. 409.

[38] G. HELLWIG, *Partial Differential Equations* (Waltham: Blaisdell, 1964) p. 60. (Translation from the German.)

[39] P. W. BERG and J. L. MCGREGOR, *Elementary Partial Differential Equations* (San Francisco: Holden-Day, 1964), p. 33.

CHAPTER 7

Buckling of Columns

Eᴌᴀꜱᴛɪᴄ ᴄᴏʟᴜᴍɴꜱ, plates, shells and some other structures can collapse at a modest stress level, due to an instability of the equilibrium. Viscoelastic structures display similar, but more complex phenomena, which we now shall study for the case of a simple column.

7.1. The Concept of Stability

Two definitions of stability are in common use:

Fɪʀꜱᴛ Dᴇꜰɪɴɪᴛɪᴏɴ—When a system in equilibrium is subjected to a small (infinitesimal) disturbance, it may happen that it returns to its original position when the disturbance is removed. In this case the system is in stable equilibrium.

If the system is endowed with mass and suddenly unloaded, it will not stop in the equilibrium position, but will vibrate about it. If there is no inertia, the return is immediate.

Sᴇᴄᴏɴᴅ Dᴇꜰɪɴɪᴛɪᴏɴ—A system is in stable equilibrium if there does not exist any adjacent position for which its potential energy is smaller.

Both definitions are identical for conservative systems. For a nonconservative system, the second definition becomes meaningless, since a potential energy cannot be defined. But the first definition is also not of much use. A nonconservative system, when disturbed, may never return to its original position (for example, if dry friction or plastic deformation is involved), but if a small disturbance causes only a small displacement, it is for practical purposes as safe as a stable conservative system. Therefore the stability concept will be avoided altogether in the study of the behavior of viscoelastic columns.

7.2. Inverted Pendulum

Before approaching the column problem, let us have a look at a simpler problem of the same kind, the inverted pendulum shown in Figure 7.1. A rigid, massless, and weightless bar is supported by a frictionless hinge and carries at its upper end a rigid body of weight P. This body does, necessarily, have a mass P/g, but in true stability problems mass is irrelevant, and in the slow motion of viscoelastic creep its influence is negligibly small.

In Figure 7.1a the pendulum is braced laterally by a spring of stiffness k. In the undisturbed state the pendulum is vertical and the spring is undeformed. We disturb it by tilting it slightly as shown. This extends the spring by $u = \theta l$

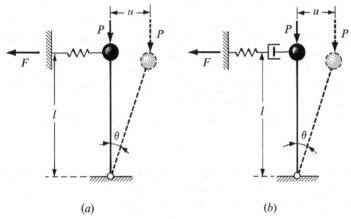

(a)   (b)

FIGURE 7.1. *Inverted pendulum.*

and produces a spring force $F = ku$. The forces P and F have moments with respect to the hinge, and the resultant moment, positive when clockwise, is

$$M = Pl\theta - Fl = (P - kl)u. \qquad (7.1)$$

If $M < 0$, that is, counterclockwise, the pendulum will return to the upright position as soon as we release it: Its equilibrium is stable. If $M > 0$, that is, if $P > kl$, then P is stronger than F, and the pendulum will tip over as soon as we stop holding it in the deflected position. Its equilibrium is unstable. In the limiting case $P = kl$, the pendulum will remain indefinitely in the disturbed position. Its equilibrium is neutral or indifferent.

In Figure 7.1b the spring has been replaced by a viscoelastic element of the Maxwell type. The relation between the force and the displacement is now

$$F + p_1\dot{F} = q_1\dot{u}.$$

Since it contains time derivatives, it matters *how* we disturb the system.

In the undisturbed state the pendulum is again vertical and $F = 0$. We apply the same disturbance as before, and we apply it suddenly. Then the dashpot has no time to act, and $F = (q_1/p_1)u$. In the disturbed position there is a resultant moment

$$M = (P - q_1 l/p_1)u.$$

If $P < q_1 l/p_1$, the system will again return to the undisturbed position, and if $P > q_1 l/p_1$ it will collapse. The words "stable" and "unstable" seem meaningful. However, if $P < q_1 l/p_1$, a complete return is possible only if we release the pendulum at once. If we hold it in the deflected position for a finite time, the Maxwell element will begin to relax, and upon release the force F will be less than $q_1 u/p_1$. It may be that the system collapses immediately, and it may be that the force F is still strong enough to pull it toward the upright position, but no longer all the way. Moment equilibrium will be reached in a still slightly tilted position, in which F is still positive, and now creep will set in and the angle θ will slowly increase without bound. This indicates that the equilibrium of the pendulum is always precarious. If $P > q_1 l/p_1$, it collapses like an unstable elastic pendulum, and for smaller P the slightest disturbance will trigger a creeping collapse.

Now replace the Maxwell spring by a Kelvin spring, for which

$$F = q_0 u + q_1 \dot{u}.$$

No matter how fast or slow we move the pendulum into the disturbed position, all that counts is the last time element Δt of this process. If we hold the pendulum for however short a time at θ, then $\dot{u} = 0$ and $F = q_0 u$. The stability decision is then the same as for an elastic spring, but even for a massless pendulum the return to $\theta = 0$ is not a quick jerk, but a slow creep.

7.3. Elastic Column

Let us quickly review the buckling of an elastic column. We start from the beam-column problem, that is, we consider a column which carries in addition to the axial load P a small lateral load p (Figure 7.2). This lateral load and the reactions that go with it produce a certain bending moment M_0, the beam moment, and a deflection w_0, and there is an additional bending moment Pw_0 from the axial load acting on w_0 as its lever arm. This causes an additional deflection δw, which in turn increases the bending moment and hence the deflection, and so on *ad infinitum*. We ask whether this infinite process converges, that is, whether there exists a positive deflection w such that the moment $M_0 + Pw$ of the external forces is in equilibrium with the moment EIw'' of the stresses.

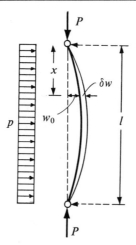

FIGURE 7.2. *Beam-column.*

The answer is shown in Figure 7.3, which represents the relation between the load P and the deflection at $x = l/2$ for fixed p. Under increasing P the deflection increases slowly at first, and then faster, and tends to infinity as P approaches the critical load $P_{cr} = EI\, \pi^2/l^2$. If p is chosen smaller, the deflection follows the dotted line, and for $p = 0$ the curve degenerates into a vertical and a horizontal part, as indicated by heavy lines. They represent the ideal column, which carries only an axial load. It remains undeflected until $P = P_{cr}$, and then it is in neutral equilibrium. The critical load is usually calculated from this neutral equilibrium of the ideal column but it is used as a base of judgement for the safety of the actual column, which may have a small lateral load as shown, or may not be perfectly straight, or may be loaded with a slight eccentricity.

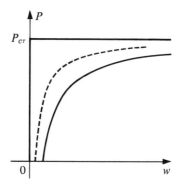

FIGURE 7.3. *Deflection of an elastic beam-column.*

7.4. Viscoelastic Column

We consider again a straight column carrying an axial load P. Its deformation consists of an axial strain, which is unimportant for our problem and which will be disregarded. At $t = 0$ we apply in addition a lateral load, which we assume in the form

$$p(x, t) = q \sin \frac{\pi x}{l} \cdot \Delta(t).$$

It produces the beam moment

$$M_0 = \frac{ql^2}{\pi^2} \sin \frac{\pi x}{l} \cdot \Delta(t),$$

and again there is an additional bending moment caused by the axial load. Let the total deflection be w; then the total bending moment is

$$M = \frac{ql^2}{\pi^2} \sin \frac{\pi x}{l} \cdot \Delta(t) + Pw, \tag{7.2}$$

and this must be introduced on the right-hand side of (4.11). This yields the differential equation of our problem:

$$I\mathbf{Q}(w'') + P\mathbf{P}(w) = - \frac{ql^2}{\pi^2} \sin \frac{\pi x}{l} \cdot \mathbf{P}\Delta(t). \tag{7.3}$$

It is satisfied by the product solution

$$w(x, t) = W(t) \sin \frac{\pi x}{l}, \tag{7.4}$$

which reduces it to an ordinary differential equation for W:

$$\frac{I\pi^2}{l^2} \mathbf{Q}(W) - P\mathbf{P}(W) = \frac{ql^2}{\pi^2} \mathbf{P}\Delta(t), \tag{7.5}$$

or, in more detail,

$$\frac{I\pi^2}{l^2} \sum_0^n q_k \frac{d^k W}{dt^k} - P \sum_0^m p_k \frac{d^k W}{dt^k} = \frac{ql^2}{\pi^2} \sum_0^m p_k \frac{d^k \Delta(t)}{dt^k}. \tag{7.6}$$

The summation on the right-hand side contains the unit step function, the Dirac function, and its derivatives, that is, functions with singularities of increasing order at $t = 0$. For $t > 0$ all these functions except $\Delta(t)$ are zero, and the right-hand side is then a constant.

We have seen (p. 19) that viscoelastic materials may be classified as solids and fluids, and as those with and without an initial elastic response to the application of a load. For the solids $q_0 \neq 0$, for the fluids $q_0 = 0$. An initial elastic response occurs when $n = m$, and it is missing when $n = m + 1$. In

(7.6), we may replace the summation limit m by n and still include all these cases if we reserve the right to let either $p_n = 0$ or $q_0 = 0$, or both.

When we integrate $d^k W/dt^k$ from 0^- to some variable upper limit t, we obtain $d^{k-1}W/dt^{k-1}$ at t plus a constant of integration. When we integrate again and repeat the procedure to a total of k integrations, we obtain

$$W(t) + c_1 t^{k-1} + c_2 t^{k-2} + \cdots + c_k.$$

Except for $W(t)$, which may have a step discontinuity at $t = 0$, this is a continuous function, and the next and any following integration will yield an entirely continuous function. Its value for $t = 0^-$ or 0^+ is the same, and when $t = 0^+$ is chosen as the upper integration limit, all these integrals equal zero. Therefore, when (7.6) is integrated n times, and, in the last integral, the upper limit made $t = 0^+$, in each of the sums only the term $k = n$ survives. Since $W(0^-) = 0$, this yields

$$\left(\frac{I\pi^2}{l^2}\, q_n - P p_n\right) W(0^+) = \frac{q l^2}{\pi^2}\, p_n, \tag{7.7}$$

and from this equation we find the initial value

$$W(0^+) = \frac{q l^2/\pi^2}{I q_n \pi^2/p_n l^2 - P}. \tag{7.8}$$

We may successively find starting values for time derivatives of W by integrating less than n times, but we shall omit this detail, since we can obtain the most important information without it.

Equation (7.8) is identical with that obtained for an elastic column with modulus $E_0 = q_n/p_n$, and the same conclusions can be drawn from it: If

$$P < P_i = \frac{E_0 I \pi^2}{l^2}, \tag{7.9}$$

then there is a finite positive deflection. If P comes very close to P_i, this deflection is rather large. If $P = P_i$, there exists no solution (within the limitations of the linearization underlying our equations), and the column will collapse immediately. We call this *instantaneous buckling*, and the critical load P_i is a kind of Euler load. For $P > P_i$ there exists a finite $W(0^+)$, but it is negative. It is of no practical interest, because (i) the load P will never get that high since the column will buckle before the load has reached the value P_i and because (ii) even if we could get the load high enough before applying the disturbing influence p, the column would never find this equilibrium but would bend in the positive direction, where there is no equilibrium possible.

This, however, is not the complete story. Even if $P < P_i$, unpleasant things may happen, which we shall now investigate by attempting to solve (7.6) for $t > 0$.

This equation has the particular solution

$$W_p(t) = \frac{ql^2/\pi^2}{Iq_0\pi^2/l^2 - P} = \text{const} \tag{7.10}$$

and n complementary ones of the form

$$W_j(t) = C_j e^{\lambda_j t}, \qquad j = 1, 2, \ldots, n, \tag{7.11}$$

where λ_j are the roots of the nth-degree equation

$$\sum_{k=0}^{n} \left(\frac{Iq_k\pi^2}{l^2} - Pp_k \right) \lambda^k = 0. \tag{7.12}$$

The complete solution is, of course,

$$W(t) = W_p + \sum C_j e^{\lambda_j t}, \tag{7.13}$$

and the C_j are to be determined from initial conditions at $t = 0^+$, for which we must first find besides W also the values of its time derivatives as indicated before.

For small enough P, W_p is certainly positive, and so are all the coefficients of (7.12), unless $q_0 = 0$, that is, for all solid materials. Then this equation has no sign changes and we conclude from Descartes's rule that it has no positive solutions λ_j. Then the column deflects initially to $W(0^+)$ from (7.8), which is zero if the material has no initial elastic response ($p_n = 0$), and the deflection increases gradually according to (7.13) to the asymptotic value W_p. A column under such a load P is safe. If, however, P comes close to the critical value

$$P_c = \frac{q_0 I \pi^2}{l^2} = \frac{E_\infty I \pi^2}{l^2}, \tag{7.14}$$

then W_p is very large and becomes infinite when $P = P_c$. In this case the deflection, starting from $W(0^+)$, grows beyond all bounds, and the column is unsafe. Such a gradual buckling of the column is called *creep buckling*. The same gradual collapse must be expected if any one of the roots of (7.12) becomes positive, since then not all the exponentials in (7.13) would die out with increasing time.

For fluid materials, $q_0 = 0$ leads to $P_c = 0$. Such columns will creep buckle under any axial load, no matter how small. It may, of course, be that the collapse takes a very long time. This depends on the viscoelastic constants and on the kind and magnitude of the disturbance; and it may well be that a column can, before it collapses, fulfill a useful technical function.

Exercises

7.1. A rigid body of weight W (Figure 7.4) rests on two viscoelastic supports, which are governed by a Maxwell law:

$$R + p_1 \dot{R} = q_1 \dot{u},$$

where R is the reaction exerted by the support and u the downward displacement of its upper end. Since the system has a vertical axis of symmetry, the

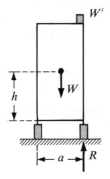

FIGURE 7.4.

rigid body will slowly sink. To find out whether this motion is sensitive to disturbances, add a small eccentric load W' and look for what happens. Are there any critical values of W or h?

7.2. Two straight bars AB and BC are connected and supported as shown in Figure 7.5. At the point C a vertical load P is applied. Study the stability

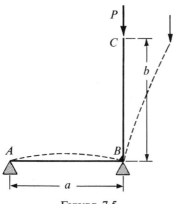

FIGURE 7.5.

of the system for the following cases: (i) AB is viscoelastic, BC is rigid; (ii) AB is elastic, BC is viscoelastic; (iii) both bars are viscoelastic. Choose any of the standard laws for the viscoelastic parts.

REFERENCES

A survey of the subject is found in the following handbook article:

[40] J. KEMPNER, "Viscoelastic Buckling," in W. Flügge (ed.), *Handbook of Engineering Mechanics* (New York: McGraw-Hill, 1962), Chap. 54.

The following paper deals with the main subject of the buckling of a straight column and the associated beam-column problem:

[41] J. KEMPNER, "Creep Bending and Buckling of Linearly Viscoelastic Columns," *NACA, Techn. Note 3136* (1954). (Considers the four-parameter fluid and materials of lower order.)

The following paper gives an example of a buckling problem involving a linear viscoelastic material in a nonlinear kinematic setting:

[42] J. HULT, "Oil Canning Problems in Creep," in N. J. Hoff (ed.), *Creep in Structures* (Berlin: Springer-Verlag, 1962), pp. 161–173.

CHAPTER 8

Viscoelasticity in Three Dimensions

THUS FAR, we have restricted our attention to problems in which there was only one stress σ (or possibly τ) and one strain ϵ (or possibly γ), and the viscoelastic law (2.23) and its equivalents (3.6), (3.7), (5.6) were appropriate to describe the behavior of the material. When there is more than one stress component, we need a generalization of the viscoelastic law, which corresponds to the three-dimensional form of Hooke's law and contains it as a special case. We shall now find a logical approach to the general constitutive equations of viscoelastic materials and then apply them to a few typical cases.

8.1. Analysis of Stress and Strain

When a small rectangular block* is cut from a body, we can define on its sides six (or rather nine) stress components, which are shown in Figure 8.1. It is well known that, for reasons of moment equilibrium, the shear stresses are equal in pairs, and we shall never have any reason to distinguish between τ_{xy} and τ_{yx}. The quantities σ_x, σ_y, ..., τ_{xz} are called *stress components*. Obviously, they are not the components of one vector, but of three vectors, and they form a physical entity, called the *stress tensor*. To display all the components of the stress tensor, we shall use matrix notation. However we shall not use in our formulas any matrix algebra beyond the addition of matrices and their multiplication by a numerical factor, and we shall not use any tensor calculus.

---

* Commonly called a parallelepipedon. It seems time that our language develop a word that is easier to pronounce and to spell than this monster.

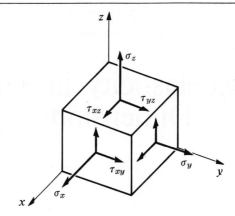

FIGURE 8.1. *Infinitesimal element of a solid body.*

As a first step in the analysis of the stress tensor, we split it into two parts:

$$\begin{bmatrix} \sigma_x & \tau_{xy} & \tau_{xz} \\ \tau_{xy} & \sigma_y & \tau_{yz} \\ \tau_{xz} & \tau_{yz} & \sigma_z \end{bmatrix} = \begin{bmatrix} s & 0 & 0 \\ 0 & s & 0 \\ 0 & 0 & s \end{bmatrix} + \begin{bmatrix} s_x & s_{xy} & s_{xz} \\ s_{xy} & s_y & s_{yz} \\ s_{xz} & s_{yz} & s_z \end{bmatrix}. \tag{8.1}$$

This matrix equation means that, for example,

$$\sigma_x = s + s_x, \qquad \tau_{xy} = 0 + s_{xy},$$

and so forth. The first stress system on the right-hand side consists of equal tensile (or compressive) stresses and no shear. The pressure inside an inviscid liquid or gas is of this kind, and therefore this stress system is called *hydrostatic stress* (also if s is a tension). The second term is, so far, simply what is left over after a hydrostatic stress has been subtracted from the given stress system. The question arises whether there is a special choice of s that would make the leftover meaningful.

We arrive at something useful when we choose

$$s = \tfrac{1}{3}(\sigma_x + \sigma_y + \sigma_z). \tag{8.2}$$

Then the sum of the three diagonal terms (the *trace* of the matrix) is the same for the first two matrices of (8.1) and, hence,

$$s_x + s_y + s_z = 0. \tag{8.3}$$

A tensor of this peculiar kind is called a *deviator*. Its components are the *stress deviations* (that is, from the average normal stress). A stress deviator can be represented as a superposition of five simple shear-stress systems:

$$
\begin{bmatrix} s_x & s_{xy} & s_{xz} \\ s_{xy} & s_y & s_{yz} \\ s_{xz} & s_{yz} & s_z \end{bmatrix} = \begin{bmatrix} 0 & s_{xy} & 0 \\ s_{xy} & 0 & 0 \\ 0 & 0 & 0 \end{bmatrix} + \begin{bmatrix} 0 & 0 & 0 \\ 0 & 0 & s_{yz} \\ 0 & s_{yz} & 0 \end{bmatrix}
$$

$$
+ \begin{bmatrix} 0 & 0 & s_{xz} \\ 0 & 0 & 0 \\ s_{xz} & 0 & 0 \end{bmatrix} + \begin{bmatrix} s_x & 0 & 0 \\ 0 & -s_x & 0 \\ 0 & 0 & 0 \end{bmatrix} + \begin{bmatrix} 0 & 0 & 0 \\ 0 & -s_z & 0 \\ 0 & 0 & s_z \end{bmatrix}. \quad (8.4)
$$

The first three matrices on the right are obviously shear systems with $s_{xy} = \tau_{xy}$, and so forth. The fourth one is a plane stress system in the x, y plane, and

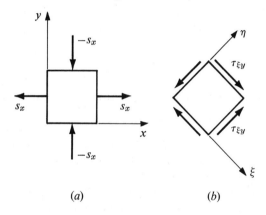

(a)   (b)

FIGURE 8.2. *Pure shear stress in different reference frames.*

it is well known that it is equivalent to shear stresses $\tau_{\xi\eta} = s_x$ in an element cut out as shown in Figure 8.2b. A similar interpretation is possible for the fifth term in (8.4).

We may now draw the following conclusions: The hydrostatic stress system has so high a degree of symmetry that the corresponding deformation can be only a change of size of the block shown in Figure 8.1. If it was a cube it will remain a cube; and a sphere cut from the material will remain a sphere. On the other hand, each of the shear systems in (8.4) can produce only a shear deformation, be it the change of an angle between two faces of a block or between two of its diagonal planes; but none of these shear stress systems will change the volume. This is true whether the deformation is elastic or unelastic, as long as it is small enough to permit linear superposition, and as long as the material is isotropic, that is, as long as it does not have any preferential directions of deformation.

We now turn to a similar analysis of the strain. There are two kinds of strain, longitudinal strain and shear strain. The longitudinal strain describes the increase of length of a line element, like ϵ_x, ϵ_y, ϵ_z. The shear strain describes a change of an angle, for example, the small decrease of the right angle between line elements dx and dy, which is called the shear strain γ_{xy}. Our equations will turn out to be simpler when we use instead of γ_{xy} the quantity

$$\epsilon_{xy} = \tfrac{1}{2}\gamma_{xy} \tag{8.5}$$

to measure the shear deformation, and we shall use the word "shear" for it.

The quantities ϵ_x, ϵ_y, ..., ϵ_{xz} are the components of the *strain tensor*. We display them also as a matrix and split it just as we did for the stresses:

$$\begin{bmatrix} \epsilon_x & \epsilon_{xy} & \epsilon_{xz} \\ \epsilon_{xy} & \epsilon_y & \epsilon_{yz} \\ \epsilon_{xz} & \epsilon_{yz} & \epsilon_z \end{bmatrix} = \begin{bmatrix} e & 0 & 0 \\ 0 & e & 0 \\ 0 & 0 & e \end{bmatrix} + \begin{bmatrix} e_x & e_{xy} & e_{xz} \\ e_{xy} & e_y & e_{yz} \\ e_{xz} & e_{yz} & e_z \end{bmatrix}. \tag{8.6}$$

Again we choose

$$e = \tfrac{1}{3}(\epsilon_x + \epsilon_y + \epsilon_z), \tag{8.7}$$

that is, equal to one third of the volume strain (bulk strain). It follows that

$$e_x + e_y + e_z = 0, \tag{8.8}$$

which indicates that the second part of the strain system describes a change of shape without a change of volume. The meaning of (8.6) is, therefore, that we have split a general strain tensor into one part which represents a pure *dilatation* (without change of shape), and into another part which represents a *distortion*, that is, a change of shape at constant volume.

Just as we could resolve the stress deviator into a superposition of five simple shear stresses, we can resolve the strain deviator into five simple shear strains:

$$\begin{bmatrix} e_x & e_{xy} & e_{xz} \\ e_{xy} & e_y & e_{yz} \\ e_{xz} & e_{yz} & e_z \end{bmatrix} = \begin{bmatrix} 0 & e_{xy} & 0 \\ e_{xy} & 0 & 0 \\ 0 & 0 & 0 \end{bmatrix} + \begin{bmatrix} 0 & 0 & 0 \\ 0 & 0 & e_{yz} \\ 0 & e_{yz} & 0 \end{bmatrix}$$

$$+ \begin{bmatrix} 0 & 0 & e_{xz} \\ 0 & 0 & 0 \\ e_{xz} & 0 & 0 \end{bmatrix} + \begin{bmatrix} e_x & 0 & 0 \\ 0 & -e_x & 0 \\ 0 & 0 & 0 \end{bmatrix} + \begin{bmatrix} 0 & 0 & 0 \\ 0 & -e_z & 0 \\ 0 & 0 & e_z \end{bmatrix}. \tag{8.9}$$

The first three matrices on the right-hand side obviously represent simple shears. The fourth one is a deformation in the x, y plane, which is illustrated in Figure 8.3. To produce the deformation, we keep O at rest and let A move

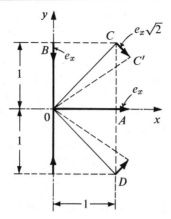

FIGURE 8.3. *Pure shear strain in different reference frames.*

to the right by a distance e_x, while B moves as much downward. The point C has the vector sum of both these displacements and hence moves by a distance $CC' = e_x\sqrt{2}$ as shown. The diagonal OC rotates through the angle $e_x\sqrt{2}/\sqrt{2} = e_x$, and the right angle COD decreases by $2e_x$. In a coordinate system ξ, η (Figure 8.2) this is a simple shear with

$$\epsilon_{\xi\eta} = \tfrac{1}{2}\gamma_{\xi\eta} = e_x.$$

8.2. The Viscoelastic Law

If a viscoelastic material is isotropic, a hydrostatic stress must produce a dilatation and no distortion. The quantities s and e may be connected by a relation like (2.23) or any of its equivalents. We write

$$\sum_0^{m''} p_k'' \frac{d^k s}{dt^k} = \sum_0^{n''} q_k'' \frac{d^k e}{dt^k} \qquad (8.10a)$$

or, shorter,

$$\mathbf{P}'' s = \mathbf{Q}'' e. \qquad (8.10b)$$

On the other hand, each of the five shear stress systems in (8.4) must produce the shear strain represented by the corresponding matrix in (8.9), and isotropy of the material requires that the relation be the same for all these pairs. We write it in the form

$$\sum_0^{m'} p_k' \frac{d^k S}{dt^k} = \sum_0^{n'} q_k' \frac{d^k E}{dt^k} \qquad (8.11a)$$

or

$$\mathbf{P}' S = \mathbf{Q}' E, \qquad (8.11b)$$

where S and E stand for corresponding components of stress and strain deviators or, if we wish, for the entire matrices on the left-hand side of (8.4) and (8.9).

The four operators $\mathbf{P}''$, $\mathbf{Q}''$, $\mathbf{P}'$, $\mathbf{Q}'$, which describe the viscoelastic behavior of the material, are entirely independent of each other. To each pair of them Table 2.2 is applicable. We shall standardize them so that $p_0'' = p_0' = 1$.

The elastic solid is a limiting case of the viscoelastic materials. We may write the linear elastic law (that is, Hooke's law) in the form (8.10a), (8.11a). The cubic dilatation $3e$ is proportional to the hydrostatic part of the stress, and each shear component to the corresponding shear stress:

$$s = K{\cdot}3e, \qquad \tau_{xy} = G{\cdot}2\epsilon_{xy}. \tag{8.12}$$

Here K is the bulk modulus and G the shear modulus. We see that for the elastic solid the four operators are simple multiplicative constants:

$$\mathbf{P}'' = 1, \qquad \mathbf{Q}'' = 3K, \qquad \mathbf{P}' = 1, \qquad \mathbf{Q}' = 2G.$$

Since all components of the stress deviator are subject to the same law, we have now

$$\begin{aligned}
\sigma_x &= s + s_x = 3Ke + 2Ge_x \\
&= 3K{\cdot}\tfrac{1}{3}(\epsilon_x + \epsilon_y + \epsilon_z) + 2G[\epsilon_x - \tfrac{1}{3}(\epsilon_x + \epsilon_y + \epsilon_z)] \\
&= (K + \tfrac{4}{3}G)\epsilon_x + (K - \tfrac{2}{3}G)(\epsilon_y + \epsilon_z).
\end{aligned}$$

The usual formulation of this law reads

$$\sigma_x = \frac{E}{(1 + \nu)(1 - 2\nu)}\,[(1 - \nu)\epsilon_x + \nu(\epsilon_y + \epsilon_z)].$$

A comparison of the coefficients of both formulas leads to relations between the elastic modulus E and Poisson's ratio ν on the one side and K and G on the other:

$$E = \frac{9KG}{3K + G}, \qquad \nu = \frac{1}{2}\frac{3K - 2G}{3K + G}. \tag{8.13}$$

8.3. Uni-axial Stress

The viscoelastic law (8.10), (8.11) is a new and more general formulation of the constitutive equations of materials. When applied to the special case of simple tension, it must lead back to (2.23) and to a relation between its operators $\mathbf{P}$, $\mathbf{Q}$ and the four new ones.

In uni-axial tension we have only one stress, σ_x. From (8.2) we find $s = \tfrac{1}{3}\sigma_x$, and then the stress deviations

$$s_x = \tfrac{2}{3}\sigma_x, \qquad s_y = s_z = -\tfrac{1}{3}\sigma_x.$$

The strain has three components: the axial strain ϵ_x and the lateral contractions $\epsilon_y = \epsilon_z$. From (8.7) we have then

$$e = \tfrac{1}{3}(\epsilon_x + 2\epsilon_y)$$

and, hence,

$$e_x = \tfrac{2}{3}(\epsilon_x - \epsilon_y), \qquad e_y = e_z = -\tfrac{1}{3}(\epsilon_x - \epsilon_y).$$

To these quantities we apply (8.10b) and (8.11b):

$$\mathbf{P}''(\tfrac{1}{3}\sigma_x) = \mathbf{Q}''(\tfrac{1}{3}(\epsilon_x + 2\epsilon_y)),$$
$$\mathbf{P}'(\tfrac{2}{3}\sigma_x) = \mathbf{Q}'(\tfrac{2}{3}(\epsilon_x - \epsilon_y)).$$

Since the operators are linear, we may pull the constant factors out and then cancel them, and we may also split the right-hand sides into sums:

$$\mathbf{P}''\sigma_x = \mathbf{Q}''\epsilon_x + 2\mathbf{Q}''\epsilon_y, \tag{8.14a}$$
$$\mathbf{P}'\sigma_x = \mathbf{Q}'\epsilon_x - \mathbf{Q}'\epsilon_y. \tag{8.14b}$$

We now apply the operator $\mathbf{Q}'$ to the first equation and $2\mathbf{Q}''$ to the second and add:

$$(\mathbf{Q}'\mathbf{P}'' + 2\mathbf{Q}''\mathbf{P}')\sigma_x = (\mathbf{Q}'\mathbf{Q}'' + 2\mathbf{Q}''\mathbf{Q}')\epsilon_x + 2(\mathbf{Q}'\mathbf{Q}'' - \mathbf{Q}''\mathbf{Q}')\epsilon_y.$$

It is now important to know that the operators are not only linear, but that their coefficients p_k'', q_k'', p_k', q_k' are independent of time. Then

$$\mathbf{Q}''\mathbf{Q}'\epsilon_y = \mathbf{Q}'\mathbf{Q}''\epsilon_y,$$

that is, the operators are commutative, and the ϵ_y term in our last equation vanishes. Thus we have

$$(\mathbf{P}''\mathbf{Q}' + 2\mathbf{Q}''\mathbf{P}')\sigma_x = 3\mathbf{Q}''\mathbf{Q}'\epsilon_x. \tag{8.15a}$$

This is identical with (2.23) if we set

$$\mathbf{P} = \mathbf{P}''\mathbf{Q}' + 2\mathbf{Q}''\mathbf{P}', \qquad \mathbf{Q} = 3\mathbf{Q}''\mathbf{Q}'. \tag{8.16}$$

By a quite similar operation we may eliminate ϵ_x between (8.14) to obtain a relation governing the lateral contraction ϵ_y:

$$(\mathbf{P}''\mathbf{Q}' - \mathbf{Q}''\mathbf{P}')\sigma_x = 3\mathbf{Q}''\mathbf{Q}'\epsilon_y. \tag{8.15b}$$

Equations (8.15) are the viscoelastic equivalent of a complete statement of Hooke's law for uni-axial tension. To interpret them, we shall now inspect a number of special choices for the operators.

While the shear deformation may be rather large, the change of volume measured by e is always very limited. It seems, therefore, reasonable to neglect the latter completely and to assume $e = 0$. This corresponds to $\mathbf{P}'' = 0$, $\mathbf{Q}'' = 1$. The constitutive equations for uni-axial stress are then

$$2\mathbf{P}'\sigma_x = 3\mathbf{Q}'\epsilon_x, \qquad -\mathbf{P}'\sigma_x = 3\mathbf{Q}'\epsilon_y.$$

They show that at all times $\epsilon_y = -\tfrac{1}{2}\epsilon_x$.

The next best approximation to a real material would be to assume that the dilatation is elastic:

$$s = 3Ke.$$

This corresponds to $\mathbf{P}'' = 1$, $\mathbf{Q}'' = 3K$, and (8.15) are now

$$(\mathbf{Q}' + 6K\mathbf{P}')\sigma_x = 9K\mathbf{Q}'\epsilon_x, \tag{8.17a}$$

$$(\mathbf{Q}' - 3K\mathbf{P}')\sigma_x = 9K\mathbf{Q}'\epsilon_y. \tag{8.17b}$$

The choice of the distortion operators $\mathbf{P}'$, $\mathbf{Q}'$ is still free, and we shall inspect two possibilities.

First, we assume a Maxwell law for the distortion, letting

$$\mathbf{P}' = 1 + p_1' \frac{d}{dt}, \qquad \mathbf{Q}' = q_1' \frac{d}{dt}. \tag{8.18}$$

When we introduce this in (8.17) and collect terms, we find the following pair of equations:

$$6K\sigma_x + (q_1' + 6Kp_1')\dot{\sigma}_x = 9Kq_1'\dot{\epsilon}_x, \tag{8.19a}$$

$$-3K\sigma_x + (q_1' - 3Kp_1')\dot{\sigma}_x = 9Kq_1'\dot{\epsilon}_y. \tag{8.19b}$$

Both have the form of the Maxwell equation. In (8.19a) we divide by $6K$ and extract the coefficients

$$p_1 = p_1' + q_1'/6K, \qquad q_1 = \tfrac{3}{2}q_1',$$

and similarly from (8.19b)

$$p_1^* = p_1' - q_1'/3K, \qquad q_1^* = -3q_1'.$$

We may use these coefficients in all formulas which Table 2.2 gives for the Maxwell material. In particular for unit step loading $\sigma_x = \Delta(t)$, we can describe the strains by two creep compliances

$$\epsilon_x = J_x(t), \qquad \epsilon_y = J_y(t),$$

formed from the coefficients according to the formula for $J(t)$ in Table 2.2. We find

$$J_x(t) = \frac{p_1 + t}{q_1} = \frac{2p_1'}{3q_1'} + \frac{1}{9K} + \frac{2t}{3q_1'}, \tag{8.20a}$$

$$J_y(t) = \frac{p_1^* + t}{q_1^*} = -\frac{p_1'}{3q_1'} + \frac{1}{9K} - \frac{t}{3q_1'}. \tag{8.20b}$$

These compliances have been plotted in Figure 8.4. The plot shows that the ratio $\epsilon_x/(-\epsilon_y)$ varies with time, which indicates that the concept of a Poisson ratio is not very meaningful for a viscoelastic material.

Now let us compare these results with those for another viscoelastic material. We again assume that it is elastic in dilatation, but postulate the Kelvin law for distortion. We have then to introduce in (8.17) the operators

$$\mathbf{P}' = 1, \qquad \mathbf{Q}' = q_0' + q_1' \frac{d}{dt}$$

and this leads to the following constitutive equations:

$$(q_0' + 6K)\sigma_x + q_1'\dot{\sigma}_x = 9K(q_0'\epsilon_x + q_1'\dot{\epsilon}_x), \qquad (8.21a)$$

$$(q_0' - 3K)\sigma_x + q_1'\dot{\sigma}_x = 9K(q_0'\epsilon_y + q_1'\dot{\epsilon}_y). \qquad (8.21b)$$

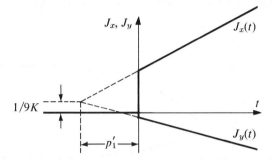

FIGURE 8.4. *Creep compliances for a material with elastic dilatation and Maxwell distortion.*

These equations are not of the Kelvin type; they have the same form as (2.19), which describes the three-parameter solid. This is understandable, since a material which has elastic dilatation must have an impact response, which the Kelvin solid is lacking.

After dividing each equation by the coefficient of σ_x and then comparing it with (2.19), we may read from it a set of coefficients. For (8.21a) they are

$$p_1 = \frac{q_1'}{q_0' + 6K}, \qquad q_0 = \frac{9Kq_0'}{q_0' + 6K}, \qquad q_1 = \frac{9Kq_1'}{q_0' + 6K}$$

and for (8.21b), which controls the transverse strain,

$$p_1^* = \frac{q_1'}{q_0' - 3K}, \qquad q_0^* = \frac{9Kq_0'}{q_0' - 3K}, \qquad q_1^* = \frac{9Kq_1'}{q_0' - 3K}.$$

With these we enter the formula for the creep compliance $J(t)$ of the three-parameter solid in Table 2.2 and find with $q_0/q_1 = q_0^*/q_1^* = q_0'/q_1' = \lambda$ for the axial strain

$$J_x(t) = \frac{1}{9K} e^{-\lambda t} + \left(\frac{1}{9K} + \frac{2}{3q_0'}\right)(1 - e^{-\lambda t}) \qquad (8.22a)$$

and for the transverse strain

$$J_y(t) = \frac{1}{9K} e^{-\lambda t} + \left(\frac{1}{9K} - \frac{1}{3q_0'}\right)(1 - e^{-\lambda t}). \qquad (8.22b)$$

These creep compliances are plotted in Figure 8.5. The curves show that the material is solid; both strains tend asymptotically toward finite limits. In addition, the curves show a rather surprising feature: For $t = 0^+$, both compliances are positive. This means that upon a sudden application of load to a tension bar, its first response is that it gets not only longer, but also thicker! This is a necessary consequence of the combination of elastic dilatation (with impact response) and Kelvin distortion (without it). The first thing the bar

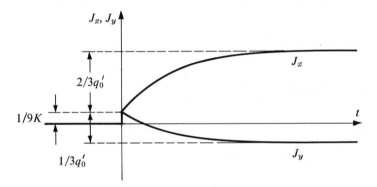

FIGURE 8.5. *Creep compliances for a material with elastic dilatation and Kelvin distortion.*

does is to increase its volume—equally in all directions—and then distortional creep sets in, which makes the bar longer and thinner without further change of its volume. Although the "negative lateral contraction," if we may call it so, looks improbable, there seems to be no physical law standing against it.

8.4. Viscoelastic Cylinder in a Rigid Die

We are now prepared to solve a simple problem. A cylindrical sample of an arbitrary viscoelastic material is inserted in a die and loaded by a pressure p as shown in Figure 8.6. The axis of the cylinder is the x axis, and there are y and z axes in some horizontal plane. If we assume that there is no friction between the cylinder and the die, the stresses are the same at all points. They consist of a compression $\sigma_x = -p$ and of equal, but still unknown, stresses $\sigma_y = \sigma_z$. The die confines the sample horizontally so that $\epsilon_y = \epsilon_z = 0$, but there is, of course, a strain ϵ_x, which we expect to be negative. The unknowns of our problem are σ_y and ϵ_x.

We formulate differential equations by expressing each of the strains as the superposition of contributions caused by σ_x, σ_y, and σ_z, that is by applying repeatedly (8.15).

If there were only the stress σ_x, then ϵ_x would be related to it by (8.15a). For a stress σ_y, acting alone, ϵ_x is a transverse strain and the relation between the two is (8.15b), modified by interchanging the subscripts x and y. The stress σ_z makes another contribution of the same magnitude. Adding the three contributions to $3\mathbf{Q}''\mathbf{Q}'\epsilon_x$ obtained in this way, we have

$$(\mathbf{P}''\mathbf{Q}' + 2\mathbf{Q}''\mathbf{P}')\sigma_x + 2(\mathbf{P}''\mathbf{Q}' - \mathbf{Q}''\mathbf{P}')\sigma_y = 3\mathbf{Q}''\mathbf{Q}'\epsilon_x. \qquad (8.23a)$$

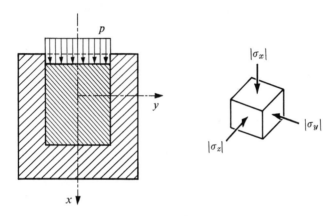

FIGURE 8.6. *Viscoelastic cylinder in a rigid die.*

In the same way we obtain an equation for ϵ_y, noting that now σ_y is the stress that acts in the same direction, while for σ_x and σ_z, ϵ_y is a transverse strain. We find

$$(\mathbf{P}''\mathbf{Q}' + 2\mathbf{Q}''\mathbf{P}')\sigma_y + (\mathbf{P}''\mathbf{Q}' - \mathbf{Q}''\mathbf{P}')(\sigma_x + \sigma_z) = 3\mathbf{Q}''\mathbf{Q}'\epsilon_y,$$

which, with $\sigma_z = \sigma_y$, may be simplified to read

$$(2\mathbf{P}''\mathbf{Q}' + \mathbf{Q}''\mathbf{P}')\sigma_y + (\mathbf{P}''\mathbf{Q}' - \mathbf{Q}''\mathbf{P}')\sigma_x = 3\mathbf{Q}''\mathbf{Q}'\epsilon_y.$$

Since we know that $\epsilon_y = 0$, this is a differential equation for our first unknown, σ_y:

$$(2\mathbf{P}''\mathbf{Q}' + \mathbf{Q}''\mathbf{P}')\bar{\sigma}_y = (\mathbf{Q}''\mathbf{P}' - \mathbf{P}''\mathbf{Q}')\bar{\sigma}_x. \qquad (8.23b)$$

After it has been solved, (8.23b) may be used to find ϵ_x.

To actually solve these equations, we subject them to the Laplace transformation. If we assume that all the initial values appearing in (2.18) are zero, this amounts to replacing the time-dependent stresses and strains by their

Laplace transforms $\bar{\sigma}$ and $\bar{\epsilon}$ and the differential operators $\mathbf{P}'$, $\mathbf{Q}'$, $\mathbf{P}''$, $\mathbf{Q}''$ by polynomials in the Laplace variable $\mathscr{A}^*$ defined as indicated in (2.26):

$$3\mathscr{Q}''\mathscr{Q}'\bar{\epsilon}_x = (\mathscr{P}''\mathscr{Q}' + 2\mathscr{Q}''\mathscr{P}')\bar{\sigma}_x + 2(\mathscr{P}''\mathscr{Q}' - \mathscr{Q}''\mathscr{P}')\bar{\sigma}_y, \quad (8.24a)$$

$$(2\mathscr{P}''\mathscr{Q}' + \mathscr{Q}''\mathscr{P}')\bar{\sigma}_y = (\mathscr{Q}''\mathscr{P}' - \mathscr{P}''\mathscr{Q}')\bar{\sigma}_x. \quad (8.24b)$$

Since in these equations everything is simple algebra, we may divide each one by the coefficient on its left-hand side [we could not have divided (8.23) by operators!] and find, after some algebra,

$$\bar{\sigma}_y = \frac{\mathscr{Q}''\mathscr{P}' - \mathscr{P}''\mathscr{Q}'}{2\mathscr{P}''\mathscr{Q}' + \mathscr{Q}''\mathscr{P}'}\,\bar{\sigma}_x, \qquad \bar{\epsilon}_x = \frac{3\mathscr{P}''\mathscr{P}'}{2\mathscr{P}''\mathscr{Q}' + \mathscr{Q}''\mathscr{P}'}\,\bar{\sigma}_x. \quad (8.25a,b)$$

Before we can complete the solution, we have to specify how σ_x is to depend on time, and we have to choose a viscoelastic material. We apply σ_x as a step load

$$\sigma_x = -p\,\Delta(t),$$

which has the transform

$$\bar{\sigma}_x = -p/\mathscr{A}, \quad (8.26)$$

and we consider now two typical materials.

Since, in this case, no deformation is possible without a change of volume, it would make no sense to consider an incompressible material. We begin, therefore, with assuming elastic behavior in dilatation and the Maxwell law for distortion, that is, $\mathbf{P}'' = 1$, $\mathbf{Q}'' = 3K$, and (8.18). The corresponding polynomials are

$$\mathscr{P}'' = 1, \qquad \mathscr{Q}'' = 3K, \qquad \mathscr{P}' = 1 + p_1'\mathscr{A}, \qquad \mathscr{Q}' = q_1'\mathscr{A},$$

and when we insert these in (8.25), we find

$$\bar{\sigma}_y = -\frac{p}{\mathscr{A}}\frac{3K(1 + p_1'\mathscr{A}) - q_1'\mathscr{A}}{3K(1 + p_1'\mathscr{A}) + 2q_1'\mathscr{A}},$$

$$\bar{\epsilon}_x = -\frac{p}{\mathscr{A}}\frac{3(1 + p_1'\mathscr{A})}{3K(1 + p_1'\mathscr{A}) + 2q_1'\mathscr{A}}.$$

With the abbreviations

$$1/\alpha = 3K, \qquad 1/\lambda = p_1' + 2\alpha q_1'$$

---

* The reader will notice that here the symbol for the Laplace variable has been changed from s to $\mathscr{A}$. This has been necessary, because we shall soon (p. 111) find in the same equation the Laplace variable $\mathscr{A}$ and the hydrostatic stress s and it does not seem wise to depart in the choice of symbols for either one very far from generally accepted usage.

these expressions may be rewritten in the following form:

$$\bar{\sigma}_y = -\lambda p\left[\frac{1}{\delta(\delta + \lambda)} + \frac{p_1' - \alpha q_1'}{\delta + \lambda}\right],$$

$$\bar{\epsilon}_x = -\frac{\lambda p}{K}\left[\frac{1}{\delta(\delta + \lambda)} + \frac{p_1'}{\delta + \lambda}\right],$$

and now we may use the transform pairs (3) and (4) of Table 2.1 to find the physical quantities σ_y and ϵ_x. They are, for $t > 0$,

$$\sigma_y = -p\left[1 - \frac{3q_1'}{3Kp_1' + 2q_1'}e^{-\lambda t}\right], \qquad (8.27a)$$

$$\epsilon_x = -\frac{p}{K}\left[1 - \frac{2q_1'}{3Kp_1' + 2q_1'}e^{-\lambda t}\right]. \qquad (8.27b)$$

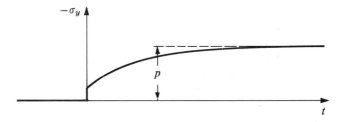

FIGURE 8.7. *Lateral pressure in a die, elastic dilatation, Maxwell distortion.*

The stress $-\sigma_y$ is the pressure which the sample exerts on the cylindrical surface of the die. It is shown in Figure 8.7 as a function of time. At $t = 0^+$ it begins with the value

$$-\sigma_y(0^+) = p\frac{3Kp_1' - q_1'}{3Kp_1' + 2q_1'},$$

which is less than p, and it increases asymptotically to p. The strain ϵ_x behaves similarly. Although the material is a fluid (see Figure 8.4), the strain ϵ_x is bounded, quite naturally so since even water would not show much deformation under the present circumstances. At the outset the interplay of the elastic responses in dilatation and distortion makes the material behave similar to an elastic solid, developing a lateral pressure less than p, but in the course of time the stresses approach those in an inviscid fluid with $\sigma_x = \sigma_y = \sigma_z = -p$.

As another choice, we consider now a material which combines Kelvin dilatation with Maxwell distortion:

$$\mathscr{P}'' = 1, \qquad \mathscr{Q}'' = q_0'' + q_1'' \mathit{s}, \qquad \mathscr{P}' = 1 + p_1' \mathit{s}, \qquad \mathscr{Q}' = q_1' \mathit{s}.$$

When this and $\bar{\sigma}_x$ from (8.26) are introduced in (8.25a), there comes

$$\bar{\sigma}_y = -p \left[\frac{1}{\mathit{s}} - \frac{3q_1'}{p_1' q_1'' \mathit{s}^2 + (p_1' q_0'' + q_1'' + 2q_1') \mathit{s} + q_0''} \right].$$

Now, let $\mathit{s} = -\lambda_1$ and $\mathit{s} = -\lambda_2$ be the roots of the denominator. Then it may easily be seen that λ_1 and λ_2 are always positive, and after resolution into partial fractions, transform pairs (1) and (3) of Table 2.1 may be applied to yield for $t > 0$ the stress

$$\sigma_y = -p \left[1 - \frac{3q_1'}{p_1' q_1''} \cdot \frac{1}{\lambda_1 - \lambda_2} (e^{-\lambda_2 t} - e^{-\lambda_1 t}) \right].$$

This has been plotted in Figure 8.8. At $t = 0$ the lateral pressure jumps at once to p, but then it decreases and recovers ultimately again to the full

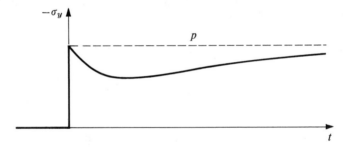

FIGURE 8.8. *Lateral pressure in a die, Kelvin dilatation, Maxwell distortion.*

hydrostatic value. This may be understood by reasoning along the following lines: Since in this system any deformation must include a change of volume, and since the Kelvin law assumed for the dilatation does not permit an immediate response, $\epsilon_x(0^+) = 0$. Now, the Maxwell law assumed for the distortion would require an immediate response, which can be avoided only if the stress deviator vanishes at $t = 0^+$, that is, when $\sigma_y = \sigma_x$. Then, as the deformation begins, it cannot be a change of volume alone and therefore stress deviations are now needed, whence $\sigma_y \neq \sigma_x$. Ultimately the presence of a Maxwell part in the deformation law requires fluid behavior, that is, $\sigma_y \to \sigma_x$.

It is left to the reader to work out the formula for $\epsilon_x(t)$. The transform pairs (3) and (4) of Table 2.1 will be needed, and the result will confirm the statements just made.

8.5. Correspondence Principle

To formulate an arbitrary stress problem, three kinds of equations are needed: the equilibrium conditions, the kinematic relations, and the constitutive law of the material. The first two of these are common to elastic and viscoelastic materials and may be found in any book on the theory of elasticity [18, 50, 51]. The equilibrium conditions describe the force equilibrium for an element $dx\,dy\,dz$ cut from the material:

$$\frac{\partial \sigma_x}{\partial x} + \frac{\partial \tau_{xy}}{\partial y} + \frac{\partial \tau_{xz}}{\partial z} + X = 0, \qquad \frac{\partial \tau_{xy}}{\partial x} + \frac{\partial \sigma_y}{\partial y} + \frac{\partial \tau_{yz}}{\partial z} + Y = 0,$$

$$\frac{\partial \tau_{xz}}{\partial x} + \frac{\partial \tau_{yz}}{\partial y} + \frac{\partial \sigma_z}{\partial z} + Z = 0, \tag{8.28}$$

where X, Y, and Z are the components of the external force per unit of volume. The kinematic relations express the strains in terms of the components u, v, and w of the displacement vector:

$$\epsilon_x = \frac{\partial u}{\partial x}, \qquad \epsilon_y = \frac{\partial v}{\partial y}, \qquad \epsilon_z = \frac{\partial w}{\partial z},$$

$$\epsilon_{xy} = \frac{1}{2}\left(\frac{\partial u}{\partial y} + \frac{\partial v}{\partial x}\right), \qquad \epsilon_{yz} = \frac{1}{2}\left(\frac{\partial v}{\partial z} + \frac{\partial w}{\partial y}\right), \qquad \epsilon_{xz} = \frac{1}{2}\left(\frac{\partial w}{\partial x} + \frac{\partial u}{\partial z}\right). \tag{8.29}$$

The constitutive equations do, of course, depend on the material. For an elastic body we have stated them in (8.12) and restate them here in the notation used in (8.11b):

$$s = 3Ke, \qquad S = 2GE. \tag{8.30a, b}$$

For viscoelastic materials, we use instead (8.10b) and (8.11b).

In an elastic body under constant load, nothing depends on time. In a viscoelastic body all the stresses, strains, and displacements occurring in (8.28), (8.29), (8.10b), and (8.11b) are time dependent, and we may subject these equations to the Laplace transformation. In (8.28) and (8.29) this amounts to replacing $\sigma_x, \ldots \epsilon_x, \ldots u, \ldots$ by $\bar{\sigma}_x, \ldots \bar{\epsilon}_x, \ldots \bar{u}, \ldots$, but in (8.10b) and (8.11b) we must also replace the differential operators $\mathbf{P}$, $\mathbf{Q}$ by the polynomials $\mathscr{P}(\delta)$, $\mathscr{Q}(\delta)$ and, hence, have the following equations

$$\mathscr{P}''(\delta) \cdot \bar{s} = \mathscr{Q}''(\delta) \cdot \bar{e}, \tag{8.31a}$$

$$\mathscr{P}'(\delta) \cdot \bar{S} = \mathscr{Q}'(\delta) \cdot \bar{E}. \tag{8.31b}$$

These are algebraic relations, and they become identical with their elastic counterparts (8.30) if we make the following substitutions:

$$3K \to \frac{\mathscr{Q}''(\delta)}{\mathscr{P}''(\delta)}, \qquad 2G \to \frac{\mathscr{Q}'(\delta)}{\mathscr{P}'(\delta)}. \tag{8.32a,b}$$

This leads us to the following, most general, form of the correspondence principle: If the solution of an elastic problem is known, the Laplace transform of the solution to the corresponding viscoelastic problem may be found by replacing the elastic constants K and G according to (8.32) by quotients of operator polynomials, and the actual loads by their Laplace transforms.

Since in most cases the solutions of elastic problems are not written in terms of the bulk modulus K and the shear modulus G, but rather in terms of Young's modulus E and Poisson's ratio v, we introduce the right-hand sides of (8.32a and b) into the right-hand sides of (8.13) to find the substitutions

$$E \rightarrow \frac{3\,\mathcal{Q}'\,\mathcal{Q}''}{2\mathcal{P}'\,\mathcal{Q}'' + \mathcal{Q}'\,\mathcal{P}''}\,, \qquad v \rightarrow \frac{\mathcal{P}'\,\mathcal{Q}'' - \mathcal{Q}'\,\mathcal{P}''}{2\mathcal{P}'\,\mathcal{Q}'' + \mathcal{Q}'\,\mathcal{P}''}\,. \qquad (8.32\text{c,d})$$

If several viscoelastic materials are involved, the corresponding elastic problem has several elastic materials with different elastic constants.

This form of the correspondence principle is of a sweeping generality, but it does have its limitations. There are cases in which a Laplace transformation is not possible, in particular the following two:

(i) It may be that a point on the boundary of a viscoelastic body is first kept free of stress, while loads are being applied elsewhere, and that after some time a device is applied which makes this point undergo a prescribed displacement. Then neither the surface traction nor the displacement is known at *all* times $t > 0$, and neither of these functions can be subjected to the Laplace transformation.

(ii) The boundaries of a viscoelastic body may be changing in the course of time. Examples are a burning mass of rocket fuel, a melting body, or one solidifying from a melt. A body extruded from an orifice (see Exercise 4.8) also belongs in this class.

The fact that in most cases a correspondence to an elastic problem exists, does not mean, of course, that one has to use the correspondence principle when dealing with a stress problem in viscoelasticity. If the elastic solution is not readily available, a direct approach may be preferable.

8.6. Two-Dimensional Problems

As an example for the application of the correspondence principle, we shall now derive the constitutive equations for two-dimensional stress problems. There are two such problems, commonly known as plane stress and plane strain.

In plane stress we are dealing with a thin slab (thickness h), which is exposed to forces lying in its middle plane. Let this by the x, y plane, then

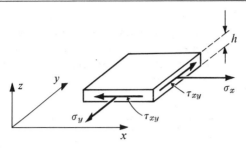

FIGURE 8.9. *Slab element, plane stress.*

the stresses σ_z and τ_{xz}, τ_{yz} are all zero, and we have only the stresses shown in Figure 8.9. Hooke's law reads then as follows:

$$E\epsilon_x = \sigma_x - \nu\sigma_y, \qquad E\epsilon_y = \sigma_y - \nu\sigma_x, \qquad G\gamma_{xy} = 2G\epsilon_{xy} = \tau_{xy}. \quad (8.33a\text{–}c)$$

When we solve (8.33) for the stresses, we have

$$\sigma_x = \frac{E}{1 - \nu^2}(\epsilon_x + \nu\epsilon_y), \qquad \sigma_y = \frac{E}{1 - \nu^2}(\epsilon_y + \nu\epsilon_x). \quad (8.34)$$

We use the correspondences (8.32b–d) to translate these equations into relations between the Laplace transforms of the stresses and strains:

$$3\mathscr{Q}'\mathscr{Q}''\bar{\epsilon}_x = (2\mathscr{P}'\mathscr{Q}'' + \mathscr{Q}'\mathscr{P}'')\bar{\sigma}_x - (\mathscr{P}'\mathscr{Q}'' - \mathscr{Q}'\mathscr{P}'')\bar{\sigma}_y,$$

$$\mathscr{P}'(\mathscr{P}'\mathscr{Q}'' + 2\mathscr{Q}'\mathscr{P}'')\bar{\sigma}_x = \mathscr{Q}'[(2\mathscr{P}'\mathscr{Q}'' + \mathscr{Q}'\mathscr{P}'')\bar{\epsilon}_x + (\mathscr{P}'\mathscr{Q}'' - \mathscr{Q}'\mathscr{P}'')\bar{\epsilon}_y],$$

$$\mathscr{Q}'\bar{\epsilon}_{xy} = \mathscr{P}'\bar{\tau}_{xy}. \quad (8.35)$$

When in these equations the polynomials $\mathscr{Q}(\lambda)$, ..., are replaced by the differential operators $\mathbf{Q}$, ..., and $\bar{\epsilon}$, $\bar{\sigma}$ by the time-dependent physical quantities ϵ, σ, one has differential equations of the same type as (2.23c), and these are the constitutive relations of plane stress.

In plane strain we start from a very long cylinder or prism extending in z direction (Figure 8.10), and we postulate that all external forces are uniformly

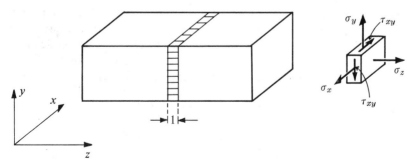

FIGURE 8.10. *Element in plane strain.*

distributed in that direction. This applies not only to the loads, but also to reactions at supports. Then all stresses, strains, and displacements must be independent of z, and there is, in particular, no strain ϵ_z. When we cut a slice from the cylinder, we find in it the same stresses σ_x, σ_y, τ_{xy} as in Figure 8.9, but also a stress σ_z needed to keep

$$\epsilon_z = \frac{1}{E}(\sigma_z - \nu\sigma_x - \nu\sigma_y) = 0.$$

When one solves this equation for σ_z and introduces the result into its companion equations for ϵ_x and ϵ_y, he finds

$$E\epsilon_x = (1 - \nu^2)\sigma_x - \nu(1 + \nu)\sigma_y, \tag{8.36a}$$

$$E\epsilon_y = (1 - \nu^2)\sigma_y - \nu(1 + \nu)\sigma_x \tag{8.36b}$$

and, solving for the stresses:

$$\sigma_x = \frac{E}{(1 + \nu)(1 - 2\nu)} [(1 - \nu)\epsilon_x + \nu\epsilon_y]. \tag{8.37}$$

The correspondence principle may again be used to find the corresponding relations for viscoelastic materials. For the physical quantities they are

$$(2\mathbf{P'Q''} + \mathbf{Q'P''})\mathbf{Q'}\epsilon_x = (\mathbf{P'Q''} + 2\mathbf{Q'P''})\mathbf{P'}\sigma_x - (\mathbf{P'Q''} - \mathbf{Q'P''})\mathbf{P'}\sigma_y, \tag{8.38}$$

and

$$3\mathbf{P'P''}\sigma_x = (\mathbf{P'Q''} + 2\mathbf{Q'P''})\epsilon_x + (\mathbf{P'Q''} - \mathbf{Q'P''})\epsilon_y \tag{8.39}$$

and similar equations for ϵ_y and σ_y. The relation between τ_{xy} and ϵ_{xy} is the same as in plane stress.

8.7. Thick-walled Tube

As an example for plane strain, we choose the thickwalled tube (Figure 8.11). In the plane of the cross section we use a polar coordinate system r, θ and normal to it we have a z axis. Continuity of the deformation demands that $\epsilon_z = 0$. The theory of elasticity yields the following formulas for the stresses defined in Figure 8.11 and for the radial displacement u:

$$\sigma_r = A - Br^{-2}, \qquad \sigma_\theta = A + Br^{-2},$$

$$u = \frac{1 + \nu}{E}[A(1 - 2\nu)r + Br^{-1}]. \tag{8.40a–c}$$

We use these formulas to solve two problems.

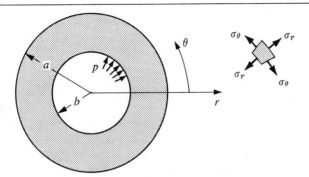

FIGURE 8.11. *Thick-walled tube.*

First, we apply an internal pressure p while keeping the outside of the tube free from stress. We have then the boundary conditions

$$r = b: \qquad \sigma_r = -p,$$
$$r = a: \qquad \sigma_r = 0.$$

Upon inserting σ_r from (8.40a) into them, we find

$$A = \frac{pb^2}{a^2 - b^2}, \qquad B = \frac{pa^2b^2}{a^2 - b^2},$$

and hence

$$\sigma_r = \frac{pb^2}{a^2 - b^2}\left(1 - \frac{a^2}{r^2}\right), \qquad \sigma_\theta = \frac{pb^2}{a^2 - b^2}\left(1 + \frac{a^2}{r^2}\right),$$
$$u = \frac{(1 + \nu)pb^2}{E(a^2 - b^2)}\left[(1 - 2\nu)r + \frac{a^2}{r}\right]. \tag{8.41a–c}$$

The stresses do not depend on the elastic constants and therefore are the same when the tube is made of a viscoelastic material. To find the displacement u of a viscoelastic tube, we apply the general correspondence principle. The substitutions (8.32c and d) lead to

$$\bar{u} = \frac{\bar{p}b^2}{a^2 - b^2}\frac{\mathscr{P}'}{\mathscr{Q}'}\left[\frac{3\mathscr{Q}'\mathscr{P}''}{2\mathscr{P}'\mathscr{Q}'' + \mathscr{Q}'\mathscr{P}''}r + \frac{a^2}{r}\right]. \tag{8.42}$$

We now apply this relation to specific materials and begin with one that is elastic in dilatation and shows Kelvin behavior in distortion:

$$\mathscr{P}'' = 1, \qquad \mathscr{Q}'' = 3K, \qquad \mathscr{P}' = 1, \qquad \mathscr{Q}' = q_0 + q_1 \Delta. \tag{8.43}$$

Assuming step function loading, $p(t) = p\,\Delta(t)$, $\bar{p} = p/\Delta$, we have then

$$\bar{u}(x, \Delta) = \frac{pb^2}{a^2 - b^2}\frac{1}{\Delta}\left[\frac{3}{6K + q_0 + q_1\Delta}r + \frac{a^2}{q_0 + q_1\Delta}\frac{1}{r}\right],$$

and with the help of Table 2.1 we find easily the actual radial displacement

$$u(r, t) = \frac{pb^2}{a^2 - b^2} \left\{ \frac{3r}{6K + q_0} \left[1 - \exp\left(-\frac{(6K + q_0)t}{q_1} \right) \right] \right.$$

$$\left. + \frac{a^2}{q_0 r} \left[1 - \exp\left(-\frac{q_0 t}{q_1} \right) \right] \right\} . \quad (8.44)$$

For $t = 0$ there is no deformation at all, since, with $\epsilon_z = 0$, there can be no deformation without distortion and the Kelvin law does not admit an immediate elastic response. For $t \to \infty$, there is a finite deformation, described by the displacement

$$u(r, \infty) = \frac{pb^2}{a^2 - b^2} \left[\frac{3r}{6K + q_0} + \frac{a^2}{q_0 r} \right] ,$$

corresponding to that of an elastic material with bulk modulus K and shear modulus $G_\infty = \frac{1}{2}q_0$.

We consider a second material, which is again elastic in dilatation, but which follows the Maxwell law in distortion:

$$\mathscr{P}'' = 1, \qquad \mathscr{Q}'' = 3K, \qquad \mathscr{P}' = 1 + p_1 \mathit{s}, \qquad \mathscr{Q}' = q_1 \mathit{s}. \quad (8.45)$$

Assuming step loading as before, we have now

$$\bar{u}(r, \mathit{s}) = \frac{pb^2}{a^2 - b^2} \frac{1 + p_1 \mathit{s}}{\mathit{s}} \left[\frac{3r}{9K + (9Kp_1 + q_1)\mathit{s}} + \frac{a^2}{q_1 \mathit{s}} \frac{1}{r} \right] .$$

Transformation into the r, t plane can be done with the pairs (3), (4), and (6) of Table 2.1, yielding the following result:

$$u(r, t) = \frac{pb^2}{a^2 - b^2} \left\{ \frac{r}{3K} \left[1 - \frac{q_1}{9Kp_1 + q_1} \exp\left(-\frac{9Kt}{9Kp_1 + q_1} \right) \right] + \frac{a^2(p_1 + t)}{q_1 r} \right\} .$$

$$(8.46)$$

In this case, there is a finite initial response $u(r, 0^+)$, depending on the moduli K and $G_0 = q_1/2p_1$, and for increasing time the deformation is unbounded, since with respect to distortion the material behaves like a fluid. There is, of course, a limit to the applicability of our results, since the deformation will ultimately get so large that our linear, small-displacement theory is no longer correct.

We turn now to a second problem, assuming that the tube is again subjected to an internal pressure p, but that its outer surface is in contact with a surrounding medium so rigid that its deformation may be neglected. We have then the following boundary conditions:

$$r = b: \qquad \sigma_r = -p,$$
$$r = a: \qquad u = 0.$$

When we introduce the general solution (8.40) here and solve for the constants, we find

$$A = -\frac{pb^2}{(1-2\nu)a^2 + b^2}, \qquad B = -(1-2\nu)Aa^2,$$

and when we introduce this into (8.40), we have the solution of the elastic problem (where the upper sign is for σ_r and the lower for σ_θ):

$$\sigma_{r,\theta} = -\frac{pb^2}{(1-2\nu)a^2 + b^2}\left[1 \pm (1-2\nu)\frac{a^2}{r^2}\right],$$

$$u = \frac{pab^2(1+\nu)(1-2\nu)}{E[(1-2\nu)a^2 + b^2]}\left(\frac{a}{r} - \frac{r}{a}\right). \tag{8.47}$$

In this case the elastic constants appear not only in u, but also in the stresses. Therefore, when we apply the general correspondence principle, we shall find that the stresses in a viscoelastic tube are time dependent. Indeed, the substitutions (8.32) yield:

$$\bar{\sigma}_{r,\theta} = -\frac{\bar{p}b^2}{r^2}\frac{(2\mathscr{P}'\mathscr{Q}'' + \mathscr{Q}'\mathscr{P}'')r^2 \pm 3\mathscr{Q}'\mathscr{P}''a^2}{(2\mathscr{P}'\mathscr{Q}'' + \mathscr{Q}'\mathscr{P}'')b^2 + 3\mathscr{Q}'\mathscr{P}''a^2},$$

$$\bar{u} = \bar{p}ab^2\frac{\mathscr{P}'\mathscr{P}''}{(2\mathscr{P}'\mathscr{Q}'' + \mathscr{Q}'\mathscr{P}'')b^2 + 3\mathscr{Q}'\mathscr{P}''a^2}\left(\frac{a}{r} - \frac{r}{a}\right). \tag{8.48}$$

It will suffice to evaluate these formulas for only one specific material, the one described by (8.45). For step loading we find:

$$\bar{\sigma}_{r,\theta} = -\frac{pb^2}{r^2}\frac{1}{\mathit{s}}\frac{6Kr^2 + [(6Kp_1 + q_1)r^2 \pm 3q_1a^2]\mathit{s}}{6Kb^2 + [(6Kp_1 + q_1)b^2 + 3q_1a^2]\mathit{s}},$$

$$\bar{u} = pab^2\frac{1}{\mathit{s}}\frac{1 + p_1\mathit{s}}{6Kb^2 + [(6Kp_1 + q_1)b^2 + 3q_1a^2]\mathit{s}}\left(\frac{a}{r} - \frac{r}{a}\right).$$

Again the transformation to the x, t plane can be achieved with the help of the pairs (3) and (4) of Table 2.1. After some lengthy arithmetic the following expressions will be found:

$$\sigma_{r,\theta} = -p\left[1 - \frac{\lambda q_1 a^2(r^2 \mp b^2)}{2Kb^2r^2}e^{-\lambda t}\right],$$

$$u = \frac{pa}{6K}\left(\frac{a}{r} - \frac{r}{a}\right)\left[1 + \frac{\lambda q_1(3a^2 - b^2)}{6Kb^2}e^{-\lambda t}\right]$$

with

$$\lambda = \frac{6Kb^2}{6Kp_1b^2 + q_1(3a^2 + b^2)}.$$

The radial displacement appears in the form $f(r) \cdot g(t)$, that is, its radial distribution is always the same while its magnitude increases with time. However, the deformation is bounded, although in the preceding example the material displayed fluid behavior. This difference is caused by the external constraint, which here is exerted by the surrounding rigid medium.

The fluid character of the material manifests itself in the stresses. For $t = 0^+$, the stress distribution is similar to that in an elastic tube, while for $t \to \infty$ it tends to a simple hydrostatic stress system $\sigma_r = \sigma_\theta = -p$. Exactly as in the structure of Figures 4.8 and 4.12, this tube behaves like a system made of two materials, but here the "two materials" are the two aspects of the deformation of the only materials present: its dilatation and its distortion.

Exercises

8.1. Consider a long, thin-walled cylinder that is closed at its ends by two bulkheads. Restrict your attention to that part of the cylinder which is not affected by the local stress disturbances caused by the bulkheads. (i). Analyze stress and strain in the cylinder wall in terms of an average and a deviator. (ii). Writing operator equations for these parts, derive from them a similar equation connecting an internal pressure p and the radial displacement w.

8.2. The elastic law (8.33), (8.34) for plane stress may be used in polar coordinates by simply replacing the subscripts x, y by r, θ. This may be used for solving the following problem: An infinite plane sheet is subjected to a uni-axial stress system $\sigma_x = \text{const}$, $\sigma_y = \tau_{xy} = 0$. This stress system is disturbed by (i) a small circular hole or (ii) a small rigid inclusion of radius a. Find stresses and displacements using polar coordinates and, possibly, the solution of the corresponding elastic problem. Suggested material: elastic in dilatation, Maxwell law for distortion.

8.3. A thin spherical shell of radius a_0 and thickness h is subjected to a pressure $p = p_0 \, \Delta(t)$. The dilatation of the material is elastic and its distortion follows the Kelvin law. How does the radius a increase with time?

8.4. Use (8.38) and the kinematic relation $\epsilon_\theta = u/r$ to derive (8.42) from equations (8.41a and b).

8.5. In plane strain there is a stress σ_z which helps making $\epsilon_z \equiv 0$. When one calculates σ_z connected with (8.41), one finds that it is independent of r. Therefore, even a very long tube, if not constrained at its ends, will actually develop a plane *stress* system with $\sigma_z \equiv 0$ and $\epsilon_z = \text{const}$. The stresses σ_r, σ_θ are the same as in plane strain, but the displacement u is different. Calculate it and specialize the result for the material described by (8.43).

8.6. A thick-walled viscoelastic tube (the core) is enclosed in a thin elastic shell (the mantle), see Figure 8.12. For the core material assume elastic dilatation (bulk modulus K) and Maxwell distortion (p_1, q_1). For the mantle,

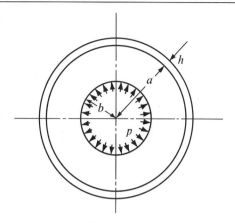

FIGURE 8.12.

use E and ν as its elastic constants. An internal pressure $p(t) = p\,\Delta(t)$ is applied at $r = b$. Find σ_r, σ_θ, and u in the core and the hoop stress σ_θ in the mantle. Assume plane strain.

REFERENCES

Papers on stress analysis in three dimensions have been numerous in recent years. The following are recommended for collateral reading:

[43] E. H. LEE, "Viscoelasticity," in W. Flügge (ed.), *Handbook of Engineering Mechanics*, (New York: McGraw-Hill, 1962), Chap. 53. (General survey.)

[44] E. H. LEE, J. R. M. RADOK, and W. B. WOODWARD, "Stress Analysis for Linear Viscoelastic Materials." *Trans. Soc. Rheology*, 3 (1959), 41–59. (Contains several cases of thickwalled cylinders.)

[45] J. R. M. RADOK, "Viscoelastic Stress Analysis." *Qu. Appl. Math.*, 15 (1957), 198–202.

The correspondence principle seems to have emerged gradually, being formulated by several authors with different, unessential limitations to its generality:

[46] T. ALFREY, "Nonhomogeneous Stress in Viscoelasticity," *Qu. Appl. Math.*, 2 (1944), 113–119. (Contains the principle for tri-axial stress and strain, but limited to an incompressible material.)

[47] W. T. READ, "Stress Analysis for Compressible Viscoelastic Materials," *J. Appl. Phys.*, 21 (1950), 671–674. (Contains the principle for compressible materials, but with reference to the Fourier transform.)

[48] M. A. BIOT, "Theory of Stress–Strain Relations in Anisotropic Viscoelasticity and Relaxation Phenomena," *J. Appl. Phys.*, 25 (1954), 1385–1391. (A very general operator formulation.)

[49] E. H. LEE, "Stress Analysis in Viscoelastic Bodies," *Qu. Appl. Math.*, 13 (1955), 183–190. (General formulation using the Laplace transformation.)

The equilibrium conditions and the kinematic relations in three-dimensional elasticity are found in Reference [18], pp. 229 and 6, respectively, and in the following books:

[50] A. E. H. Love, *A Treatise on the Mathematical Theory of Elasticity* (4th ed.), (Cambridge: Cambridge University Press, 1927 and New York: Dover Publications, 1944), pp. 85 and 38.

[51] I. S. Sokolnikoff, *Mathematical Theory of Elasticity* (2nd ed.), (New York: McGraw-Hill, 1956), pp. 41 and 22.

Index

Index

THIS BOOK WAS SET IN
TIMES ROMAN TYPE
BY THE
UNIVERSITIES PRESS.
IT WAS DESIGNED BY THE STAFF OF
BLAISDELL PUBLISHING COMPANY.